F[illegible] A VOICE

An Anthology

Edited By Nicola Monaghan

Published by

Imprimata Publishers Limited
50 Albemarle Street
London W1S 4BD

for and on behalf of The National Academy of Writing

First published 2008

A CIP Catalogue record for this book is available from the British library

ISBN 978-1-906192-13-6

Printed in Great Britain

Acknowledgements

As with all anthologies, this is a composite effort involving lots of different contributions without which this book would not have been possible.

First of all, I would like to thank the amazingly talented group of students from whose submissions this collection was created. Their enthusiasm for the project, and their hard work over the last few months in preparing their individual pieces, has been enormously exciting and encouraging to behold. In some cases, this is their first published work. I have little doubt that more success will follow for many of them.

I must also thank my colleagues Professor David Roberts and Jackie Gay for their unstinting efforts in the final days of preparing the manuscript.

Many thanks are also due to HomepageVentures and Imprimata Publishers for their donation of creative and publication services to design and produce this book.

And finally, a huge vote of thanks is due to Barry Turner and The National Academy of Writing for their ongoing support of the Diploma Course at BCU from which the current group of students is gaining so much.

Nicola Monaghan
Editor
May 2008

Contents

Life Writing

* *Contributors marked with an asterisk are tutors on the NAW course.*

Foreword

This is the first anthology from students at The National Academy of Writing. The standard they set is high but I think they would all agree that the experience of working together in the stimulating learning environment provided by the Birmingham City University has done wonders for their creative skills. The stories and poems you read here display a mature imagination, an economy of words and a clarity of thought that can only come from experiment and practice within a structured and intellectual framework.

I am enormously proud to be associated with such talent and look forward to seeing the names on the contents page appearing on other publications. I am just sorry that my nomination failed to win the prize in the Free Word Competition; but whoever said literary judgement is objective? We all have our favourites. That is what makes reading a joy and writing a thrill.

Dr. Barry Turner
Chairman
The National Academy of Writing

Fiction

Something Missing

Bobbie Darbyshire

'What do you think of it so far?'

The voice made the woman jump. It came at once from behind her and from inside her head. Had she been startled awake by a dream? She spun around.

His yellow eyes regarded her. His head floated in the shadows above a massive weight of scaly flesh. 'Seriously,' he said, 'are you having fun? Or do you find there's something missing?'

She trembled. It was a new feeling, strangely pleasant; her skin tingled and crept. She noticed where his stare was directed and moved a hand instinctively to cover herself.

Why did I do that?

'Cat got your tongue?'

'What?' She brought her spare hand up, touched tongue to fingertip. 'What do you mean?'

Through the neat, diamond-shaped hole of his mouth, a shiny, black ribbon flicked in and out. He chuckled. 'Figure of speech. My mistake. I've been around forever. I was forgetting this is only your first week.'

The gravelly drawl of his voice sent a new shiver through her body. 'I'm... I'm sorry,' she said. 'I really must be getting back. Goodbye now.'

Trying to leave fast without appearing to hurry, she felt suddenly awkward. She had to think how to move her legs: their separateness seemed wrong. She sensed on what part of her his piercing, yellow gaze was now fixed and how he would smile if she put a protective hand behind.

'Come when you get bored,' she heard him call. 'I'm always here.'

The undergrowth was damp and tangled, not like the soft turf beyond. A musky odour, sweet and repellent, rose from it as she waded through towards the sunlight. There, supine on the grass beside the spring, lay Adam, his legs carelessly apart, the sweat on his skin not yet dry.

The warm air of the glade caressed and calmed her, reminded her of her happiness. She sank down among the buttercups and, stealthily, gently, with the tip of the finger that had touched her tongue, traced the profile of Adam's face and body: his brow, his nose, his downy upper lip, the lower lip vibrating as he breathed out, the cleft in his beardless chin, his fine, smooth throat, and so on slowly down, past the fading scar on his breast, past the place where his navel might have been but wasn't, into the curls below.

He paused in his breathing, opened his clear eyes and smiled.

'That's nice,' he said. 'I'm so glad you're here. How about we do it again?'

'What do you mean, bored?' she dared to ask the serpent.

Three days had gone by. It was hot late afternoon. Ten minutes ago, she had wriggled out from under the sleeping Adam and, with thumping heart, made her way back through the tangled creepers to the steamy place where her secret friend lay coiled. Now she knelt beside him, heaping moss and fallen blossom on her thighs, covering her breasts with an arm.

He ignored her question. 'You didn't tell your mate about me.'

His eyes burned yellow. His words sent a frisson of new feeling through her. *What shall I call this one?*

'Guilt,' he supplied.

She jumped. 'Can you read my mind?'

'But of course. I know your thoughts before you think them. They're as natural as the grass growing and the birds singing. You cannot help them.'

'That's not true,' she protested. 'I don't believe you. I'm— I'm special and— and—'

'And what?'

The black tongue flickered. Out and in. She wanted to touch his scales.

'See.' She lowered arm from breast, let a knee peep through the moss. 'See, you beast. You *don't* know what I'm going to say.'

'You don't know yourself,' he whispered. 'Your brain is as empty as a blown egg.'

'It's not. It's not.' *Special and...* 'I want the exact right word.' *...beloved. What word was this?* 'Beloved. That's what I am. Special and beloved.'

He gave her a long, hard look. 'No more so than the grass and the birds. Or the water that you drink. You are as you are. Made for Adam because he was bored. And now, bored yourself.'

That word again. 'But what does it mean?'

'Early days. Early days.' He stretched his jaw in a cavernous yawn. 'Frankly, my dear, I'm finding you a wee bit boring myself. Why don't you run along now, back to old Adam?'

His eyes were cold. She leapt to her feet, naked in a shower of seeds and petals. She wanted to cry but was afraid of looking a fool. She knew that he knew everything in her head. She forced her feet to begin the long, awkward retreat, the back of her neck burning.

'That one's humiliation.' His voice came slithering after her. 'See you soon.'

'I'm damned if you will,' she muttered, and heard in the distance the first, low rumble of thunder.

'Why shouldn't we eat it, Adam?'

'Oh, I don't know,' Adam soothed. '*He* told me so. Isn't that enough?'

'Why should it be? I've never seen Him. He doesn't bother to talk to *me*.'

'Don't be foolish, sweetness. I only saw Him that one time,

before you were here. 'It's all yours,' He said. 'Nameless and wonderful.' And then He created you, nameless and wonderful too, just for me.'

She twirled a green stem in her fingers. Made the golden reflection of a buttercup dance under Adam's chin.

'Were you bored before I came?'

'How do you mean?'

She sighed. 'I don't know. Restless, not knowing what to do, wishing that something... that something a bit different would happen?'

'In what way, different? Aren't you happy?'

'Of course I am.' She leant to kiss him. 'And I love you.'

'Mmn,' he breathed, nibbling her lip. 'How do you mean?'

She pulled away. Sat back on her heels and stared into the forest.

'I don't know. It doesn't matter.'

'Hey.' He stroked her shoulder with a fig-leaf. 'Tell you what. Shall we do it again before we eat?'

'If you like.'

She rolled into his embrace. But her thoughts were elsewhere.

'I don't see *why* we shouldn't eat the fruit,' she complained to the serpent.

'It won't kill you,' he replied.

'What do you mean? Have *you* eaten it?'

'Oh yes. Oh yes, I have. Many times.'

'And did you like it?'

'It's like nothing else on earth. You're only half-alive until you've tried it. Believe me, it's an eye-opener. The day you eat it, you'll be like a god, knowing good and evil.'

'What are those?'

'Eat, and you'll know,' he answered, as he slipped away into the dark.

'That one's temptation.' His voice, more subtle than any sound she knew, naming the dryness in her mouth as he went.

Ah… God… amazing! She saw how naïve she had been. In her hand was the fruit with a single, perfect bite taken from it. She crammed the rest into her mouth, felt the cold juice run down her chin, watched it drip onto her breast.

I am beautiful. I am a goddess.

Beneath her feet the grass grew. Above her head the birds sang. They had not eaten; they continued as they were.

She ran to the spring to drink. The water had no knowledge of the fruit; it continued as it was.

She turned, and saw Adam walk from the forest into the glade. How beautiful he was! How much she loved him! But he, too, continued as he was. The sun shone in the glade. The man she loved came smiling towards her. But he didn't love her, and she was seized with a terrible new feeling.

'You want to do it,' she said.

'Yes, sweetness. How did you know?'

'You're only interested in one thing.'

'I don't understand.' He touched her cheek. 'Don't you like it? Don't you want to do it?'

'Not if you don't love me.'

He cupped her elbows. Drew her close.

'What are you saying? We must share the names of things, else who knows what a mess we'll get into.'

She pushed him away. 'You don't love me. I want you to love me, and you don't.

'What is this word?' he said. 'What do you mean?'

Suddenly she saw what must be done. 'Of course!' she cried. 'You must eat too. Then you will understand. She ran from the glade, back into the midst of the garden, to the forbidden tree. Plucked another ripe fruit. Brought it dripping in her hands.

'No,' he said.

'Trust me. You won't die. You'll understand. You will love me and thank me.'

Their fingers met. 'No,' he repeated, his eyes wide and frightened.

She slipped the fruit into his palms, breathlessly lifted his hands to his mouth. 'For me, Adam, eat.'

He bit. He chewed. He swallowed.

He choked. He coughed. He spat.

He snatched his hands from her and stared wildly around him as though for the first time.

'All lost.'

'No—.' She was shivering with terror. 'No, Adam—'

But the thunder was close now, and his eyes were as cold as the serpent's, and she knew there was no way back.

Behind the Geisha's Eyes

Robert Ronsson

The taxi dropped me at the entrance to the Grand Central Terminus. I lingered for a moment and looked up. The ceiling gets me every time. The colour. The ambition. It always makes my heart soar.

I dodged the shafts of light, broad as subway tunnels, and weaved through the scrum of commuters, down the alley between the ticketing booths and stopped at the entrance to the Vanderbilt Hall.

The swing-doors gave enough reflection for me to straighten my tie and run my fingers through thinning hair. My suit was creased but what the heck. It was Savile Row; it could take it. I smoothed the lapels, pulled in my belly, took a gulp of hot New York air and pushed open the door. I made sure I was smiling.

Frank was holding court to a gaggle of media people alongside his favourite publicity picture – the one where he's in front of the tinfoil-clad flat-iron building. As in the poster, he was swaddled in his trademark Astrakhan-collared coat. His bulk sucked in attention like a black hole. I strode over knowing the reception he'd give me.

'You're late!'

Bingo.

'Sorry, Frank. The traffic from the airport, what can I say?'

His jabbing finger was inches from my chest. 'You should have planned for it, Pete.' His hand slashed the air. 'This city! You people!'

It would have been useless to tell him the flight from London arrived an hour behind schedule.

The publicity had drawn a good-sized crowd of New York's gallery-hoppers. With the press and photographers, there must have been upwards of 400 waiting. Mind you, we could have charged for tickets with the same result. Frank's art was hot.

'Well, now you're here, Pete, we can get started.' He signalled imperiously and the arc lights cracked and buzzed. All heads turned to the podium.

I felt the familiar lurch in my chest. Sakura stood there alone. She was Frank's wife and collaborator. She wore a starched, white cotton coat down to the floor. Her tiny hands looked raw pink at the end of the tight sleeves. Her head was bowed under skeins of jet-black horse hair pinned in place by knitting needles.

Frank waved his assistant towards the podium. She carried a bucket and a paint brush. She began slapping gobbets of silver paint on the front of the coat. Was I the only one who saw Sakura flinch? The assistant smoothed the paint down, prodding and pushing with the brush. Sakura stood stiffly holding her small frame rigid.

The assistant finished and came back to stand by Frank's side. He turned to me. 'You can do the face, Pete.' He handed me a bucket and a smaller brush. 'Just whack it on. Be careful not to get too much white on the coat.' He pushed a small gauze mask into my free hand. 'Use this to protect the eyes.'

Her eyes, I thought. 'I'm only just off the plane, Frank. What about my suit?' I said.

'It's all right, Pete. You don't need any talent for this. Just slap it on. Work quickly. This stuff dries fast.'

Frank and I had met as students at the Slade in London. It didn't take me long to accept I wasn't going to make a living from painting. When Frank went into performance art I saw an opportunity to manage him and others like him. He was my first client and he was still my star – a transatlantic phenomenon. My slice of Frank gave me a good living. But he made me work for it.

I walked towards the podium. Sakura looked up. Her eyes took on the look of a deer seeing the hunter in the instant he squeezes the trigger. I dropped the brush to the floor.

Now I was centimetres from her perfect ear. I could smell the oil on her wig.

'I'll be careful, I promise,' I whispered.

She looked down at a mark in front of her paint-spotted feet.

I placed the mask over her closed eyes and pressed until the adhesive had taken. Then I put my fingers in the white paint and smoothed it over the gauze. Her eyeballs moved beneath the butterfly touch of my fingertips.

I traced a line of paint up to her forehead. I dipped for more teaspoon-sized lumps and smoothed them out leaving the paint thick to cover her dense, closely-defined eyebrows.

Her cheeks were firm. My fingers floated across her tight skin as I circled the paint over first the left side of her face then the right. I worked at my own pace, even though I could feel Frank's impatience like a spear in my back. I owed it to Sakura to make sure her faultless skin was evenly covered.

Sakura closed her mouth tightly. My arm shook with the effort to only touch her lips and not press on inside. When I pulled away, the paint formed a bridge between her lip and my finger. It held momentarily before it collapsed and a bead of white spattered at her feet.

She lifted her chin so I could paint her neck. My fingers travelled down past the hollow in her throat. I looked up as if I needed her permission to go further. I saw blank, masked eyes. Her lips had parted slightly. I put my face close so I could feel her breath.

She must have sensed her mouth was hidden from Frank. 'Thank you,' she whispered. The wind chimes in her voice made my skin fizz.

The two sides of the silver-painted coat met at her breastbone. I moved my fingers downward. Each digit left a pale smear where it sullied her cleavage. My hand trembled.

My finger was on the point of her breastbone. I looked up again and saw her tongue flick between her chalk-white lips.

I heard footsteps behind me. 'You really milked it, Pete,' Frank hissed, pushing me aside. 'Stick to your day job.'

I retreated to my place and watched. There were specks of white paint on my suit.

Now the master was at work. He had shucked off the coat and was in his shirtsleeves.

His huge hands moved quickly. He used fine-tipped brushes to put colour over the silver and the white. It was like painting a waxwork. The cameras whirred and clicked.

In less than thirty minutes a tea-house Geisha stood before us in all her finery. A silver, silk kimono was held closed by a breast-high, black-and-white patterned cummerbund. A red dragon, breathing black smoke, wound round the skirt.

The Geisha held her head high. Her rouged cheeks and cherry lips heightened her frailty. She was open-eyed and yet Sakura was blind.

Frank turned the podium through 180 degrees. We saw the back of a small woman in an incongruously large, white coat. He spun it again, with a flourish, and the Geisha was with us once more. He had given her a hand-painted fan and she held it open across her chest. It fluttered coquettishly. I sensed Sakura's eyes moving behind the mask. Was she looking for me? I shivered.

The crowd, supplemented by passers-by, hooted and clapped. Frank bowed and smirked.

The gapers and snappers dispersed and Frank drew a huddle of journalists and autograph hunters around him. He focused on the reporters. The fans would get nothing. He knew the value of his signature.

The assistant and I led Sakura behind a screen. I removed the eye-painted gauze and put it to one side. We helped her out of the coat gingerly. Frank's work had to stay intact. The studio team had a mount and frame ready. The coat, the mask and the fan would be on sale in the gallery in the morning.

Sakura was goose-pimpled in her underwear for only seconds

before she shrugged on a t-shirt. It was enough time for me to see the dark-blue smudges on her upper arms and thighs; no amount of washing would remove them. The studio and gallery teams tidied the equipment away and it was time for lunch. Frank led Sakura and me out onto 42nd Street. We turned uptown in single file.

Frank marched ahead with the sunshine falling on the back of his great, black coat. He was oblivious to the heat and to us. Sakura quick-shuffled a couple of yards behind him. She followed the path Frank battered for us through the swarm of office workers. From time to time she would turn to check I was still with her and I would see her eyelids flutter.

I followed her. I couldn't walk with her; what would I say? There was no voice for what we shared. While I was painting her face, it felt like we were building a tunnel towards each other through the great bulk of Frank. Could I make the connection real?

One second I had the thought; the next I acted on it. I grabbed Sakura by the hand and stepped into the path of a taxi. Frank continued to forge his way uptown.

'Take us to The Tribeca Grand.' It was where I always stayed. I pushed Sakura ahead of me into the cramped passenger area.

I tried to fix her with my eyes. It was all or nothing. 'You don't have to stay with him, Sakura. Neither of us does.'

She didn't speak. She just gave me those eyes, wide and limpid.

'I love you, Sakura. I know you feel the same.'

Her face distorted. I swear she was holding back tears. I took her hand.

'He'll never hurt you again,' I said.

Sakura turned away but her hand, light as a bird's wing, stayed in mine. A single tear escaped and tracked down her immaculate cheek.

She shook her head. She was looking at the stalled traffic beyond the window as she spoke.

'How can I leave him, Peter? He'd be nothing without me.'

'But he treats you like nothing ... the bruises ...'

'You don't understand.' Her tears fell freely now.

'I wouldn't do anything to harm you, Sakura.'

'That's the point, Peter. That is exactly the point.'

She knocked on the partition and gave the driver new instructions.

'You're not making sense.'

'You're a kind man, Peter. Maybe that's why you don't see it. That's the problem, you're ...' She paused to find the right word. 'You're ... harmless.'

I recoiled at the vehemence of it. Frank was waiting outside the restaurant when we pulled up. 'What happened to you?' he asked, holding the door open. 'We couldn't keep up,' I said, my voice flat.

Sakura brushed past. She touched her husband's elbow to signal he should go in. She looked up at me. I studied her lips. How I loved their texture, their firmness. The urge to take her in my arms swelled and then died as she spoke.

'You're a good man, Peter. Don't spoil things.' She smiled but her eyes were blank. She followed Frank into the restaurant.

I stood on the sidewalk in my paint-splatted suit. The sun was hot on my back. The skin on my scalp tingled. I took a deep breath and the burnt-crust smell from a nearby pretzel stall stirred my appetite. There was a subway entrance a few yards to the right. The hoarding over the entrance told me I could take an E-train to Sutphin Boulevard and connect with the AirTrain to JFK. I looked down at the fingers of my right hand and ran my thumb across the tips, trying to sense the skin of her cheek in the traces of white paint. A paper pretzel wrapper floated down and clung to my ankle. I shook my leg but it did not budge. I had to reach down to pull it away.

As I straightened I read the sign in the restaurant window, *It's air-conditioned inside*. I screwed up the wrapper and dunked it in a bin before stepping through the door. Cold air washed my face. I hurried to the table. It was Frank's treat; I didn't want them to order without me.

The Bastard Wind

Heather Wassall

'Am you sure you'm orlroight, Alan?' Lorna asks me, for the fifth time. 'Cuz you look fucking terrible. Do you want me to stop?'

The lights change to red and she pulls up with a jerk. 'Doh go throwing up in my new car!' The electric windows slide down: Lorna lights a fag. 'Tek some deep breaths!' She's a nurse, so I do as I'm told but what I really need now is the hair of the dog! Yesterday, I promised myself abstinence and an early night but then I met those old soldiers on a Falklands veteran's reunion in the hotel where I was staying and one thing led to another.

The lights change and we're off again. My head lolls back and the urban landscape unfolds. There's the new Metro station and 24 hour Asda alongside the last remaining Victorian terraced houses sprouting satellite dishes, a corner shop with the name 'Uppal' over the door where it used to be 'Johnson' and dilapidated boozers with 'lounge' and 'saloon' painted in old fashioned gold lettering on smoky glass next to fluorescent pink posters advertising Villa versus the Blues on SKY. I try to rally myself as we near my old primary school - it's been knocked down and replaced by a toy town housing estate, with car ports, postage stamp lawns and wrought iron gates. The only kid in my year to pass the 'Eleven Plus', I was. With a pang, for the first time in years, I remember Mr Harrison who encouraged me to aim high and apply to university. But I was too easily distracted by pubs and girls so I went to a teacher training college instead.

'Sorry, Mr Harrison!'

Lorna navigates an island. In the middle is a modern sculpture of jagged red metal, representing, I guess, fiery furnaces long since cooled. Now we're driving past the factory where our moms and dads spent their working lives. Once a sprawling complex, a power house of industry built up from nothing by a man with a horse and cart collecting scrap metal, I see Carmichael's is now an 'industrial estate' divided up into units manufacturing everything, it seems, from electric fires to jeans. The original entrances remain and I remember knocking-off, the sound of the bull, hundreds of people in overalls swarming out of the gates carrying duffel bags, some on bikes, some running for the bus and women office workers, clacking along in stilettos, tying brightly coloured headscarves over their beehives. My mom worked in Carmichael's offices, pushing the tea trolley around with an urn, coffee pots and jingling cups and saucers with red and gold rims.

Mom's in a home now. It's a bit smelly but they do their best, they threw a tea party for her eightieth yesterday. They say she's the life and soul of the party, has them all in stitches. 'Hello stranger!' she said. That's all I got out of her. Julie said 'Better late than never!' They were clearing away the sandwiches but I managed to grab one. 'You're a chip off the old block,' Julie said. She's still mad because I missed our dad's funeral - it was fucking years ago, Jules, get over it - I went in the pub for some Dutch courage and lost track of time. 'Two days, Alan! You went missing for two days! And now look at the state of you ....' I said, 'Nice to see you too, Jules!' We were at each other's throats so the matron asked me to leave and I would've been on the next train back to London if Lorna hadn't texted – Don't 4get N'ton tunl 2moro. Lorna sent another text this morning, she knows me so well! When the phone went off, I woke with a mouth like a builder's armpit, not knowing where I was or what I was doing there. After checking the mini bar, I switched on the TV and the whole nation was commemorating twenty-five years since the Falklands war so I couldn't forget my mate Ron's anniversary! Back in 1976, Lorna, Ron and me made a pact to walk through the tunnel again and this year I *promised* Lorna we'd do it in memory of Ron. Can't back out now - have to make up for missing Mom's party and rowing with Jules, feel like I'm really a decent guy! Make the trip worthwhile.

Lorna parks near Windmill End. I hardly recognise it! They've renovated Cob's engine house! Once, the small square brick building, with its triangular roof and 95 foot chimney housed an engine to pump water into the canal. It was derelict in the seventies when we found it. Now it's a Scheduled Ancient Monument!

Lorna pulls on a pair of bright yellow wellies. She peers through the soft morning mist, dabbing her eyes with a tissue and rubbing her nose. Is she having a little nostalgic snivel? No, not our Lorna, she's made of sterner stuff. Somehow, I get out of the car. My hands shake and I can't unpick the knots in my laces, so I scrape my shoes off and pull on a pair of Lorna's partner's wellies.

As she ambles down the path, I sneak a whisky miniature from my pocket; the sole survivor of last night's mayhem when the vets congregated in my room after the bar shut. There's a pub just down the tow path, a few hundred yards from where I'm standing but it's two hours till opening time! I wonder how long it will take to walk through the tunnel and back and whether Lorna will want to go to the pub afterwards. I take a therapeutic sip!

'Christ Almighty,' Lorna waves towards the canal. 'You'd never 'ave sin a sight like that thirty year ago!'

A family of ducks paddle by. The teeny babies, brown and yellow striped puff balls, bob merrily along in their mother's wake like corks. I hide the bottle as Lorna turns round, grinning.

'Our dad fell off his bike once, straight into the cut on his way to werk - he was bad for a wik.'

Once, the water was like tar, covered in gleaming rainbow slicks, choked by the detritus of decades, dead rats, partially submerged prams, shopping trolleys, planks of wood and once, a Mini Cooper. Now it's clear enough to see weeds on the bottom.

Lorna stands looking at the notice board above the portal. I follow; conscious of my alcohol breath as I read that Netherton canal tunnel is 3027 yards long and was completed in 1858.

'D'yow feel better now, Alan? Am you ready for this? I doh know if I am!' She emits a short, sharp smoker's rasp of a laugh, flashing her nicotine stained teeth. I see the girl in the snub nose and the gullible blue eyes.

She hadn't wanted to go through the tunnel but it was Ronnie's idea and she never liked him to get one over her, she also fancied him like mad though you'd never have guessed the way they used to bicker.

'Ooh, it brings it all back,' Lorna flaps her hands nervously. 'Did you bring a torch, Al?'

I put my hand in my pocket and touch the whisky bottle – wrong side. I pull out the puny red torch, a kiddie's toy I picked up in the paper shop yesterday, and Lorna regards it critically. 'Good lord! That's a little one, Al!'

'Size doesn't matter.'

The joke falls flat so I switch on the torch and waggle it about. This time Lorna laughs.

'Oh Al, the batteries are nearly flat! You must've left it on! Cop hold of this!'

Lorna hands me an industrial size torch to hold while she lights a cigarette. I am almost defeated by the fumes. My hand inches towards the whisky miniature but I make myself wait – I can if I have to. I can take it or leave it.

We enter the gloomy south portal and walk for several metres without torches. Water drips from the roof of the tunnel and plops into the canal with a slight echo, ripples gently disturbing the inky surface at regular intervals as if some dreadful prehistoric monster is pounding toward us like in 'Jurassic Park' ... thud ... thud ... Christ, my head's killing me!

In 1976, Ronnie was first in. He knew the way, had been before. He was adventurous, into outdoor activities: caving, climbing, hiking. Anything that involved clambering onto narrow precipices or squeezing into tiny crevices, which was ridiculous because he was a 6 foot 5 giant with size 13 shoes.

'Who else came with us?' Lorna asks. I hear a hiss when she drops her cigarette in a puddle.

'It was just you, me and Ron the first time. Then afterwards we brought Gary and Karen.'

'Whatever happened to Gary?'

'He went to the States.' As for Karen, she gave up on me years ago.

We switch on our torches. Lorna's radiates a strong beam onto the grey, dripping ceiling. Mine creates a dim, yellow circle the circumference of a toilet roll.

'Look,' Lorna says. 'Stalagmites.'

'Stalactites, C for ceiling – that's how you remember. Ron told me that.'

'Good old Ron! I can see him as if it were yesterday, in that old miner's helmet, striding along even though there wore no handrail and the path was full of holes, not like it is now!'

I notice she's gripping the sturdy rail and recall how we'd clung to the rough, perspiring walls and taken anxious steps whilst Ronnie's stride barely faltered. From time to time, he stopped to help us over a particularly perilous stretch where the towpath had crumbled away and we had to leap wide gaps where black water lapped beneath us. He gripped Lorna's elbows encouraging her to jump, spanning the abyss with his powerful legs, his back to the canal. 'Jump – c'mon, what's the matter with you - trust me!' Once my foot slipped and my boot filled up with stinking icy water. Ron thought it was hilarious. I felt a right berk. I wasn't as athletic as him.

I let Lorna walk ahead, oblivious to the distance between us. Her voice echoes off the ceiling. The torch light throws her elongated shadow across the walls. The darkness enfolds me. I open the bottle and take a swig. The alcohol scorches my throat, fills my veins with warmth and steadies my nerves, but my stomach rebels. I lean against the rail and almost retch.

'Are you listening? Al, where are you?'

'Here!' I want to sit down but force myself to catch up.

'I was saying, the ward's bin hectic lately, sometimes I wish I was back on the bench at Carmichael's – we used to have a right loff. It's all gone now! Did you see, Al? You never would have thought a big place like that would goo under. It was terrible when they laid everyone off.'

'Sent my old man crazy, he was born to work - couldn't live without it!'

'Yeh, same with marn at least he had his allotment.'

My dad had the Golden Lion! Regular as clockwork, come opening time he'd be there with his mirror and his cheese sandwiches, stayed all day. Sometimes on the way back from school, I saw him collapsed on a wall, too pissed to walk home. He never took me fishing, or to the football, on the one occasion we got drunk together we ended up fighting and Ron had to pull me off before I killed him.

I can see him now hogging the fire, bottle of Scotch standing on the hearth, glass in hand, sour expression on his face. 'Whatever yow do, son, doh follow in mah footsteps, doh goo into industry, there aye no future in it!'

But he couldn't resist making out I wasn't man enough to do real men's work.

'Call that work!' he used to call, when I got the books out. 'Yow doh know you'm born. I woren't afraid of hard werk - I was in the foundry at 14!' Like it was a badge of honour!

Once when I was a lad Dad took me and our mom down the foundry after the shut down to see where he worked. The old brick walls and furnaces were still warm and Mom couldn't get over the amount of black dust in the atmosphere. She said,

'Good heavens, Sid, I dread to think what your innerds look like after breathing in all this muck!' She was worried to death he'd get lung cancer but it was cirrhosis that got him.

'The light at the end of the tunnel, bloody hell, it looks miles away!'

There's a tiny white half moon in the far distance, like a shape cut out of black paper. It would be hours before we got back to the pub – what was it called? – I know, The Dry Dock, the bar was part of an old narrow boat.

'Are you OK? You look knackered.'

'I'm OK, honest.'

'We can goo back!'

'Nah, c'mon, Lor! Remember we're doing this for Ron!'

I stagger forward, taking myself and Lorna by surprise, taking the opportunity to slip the bottle out of my pocket. I realise there's not much left and wonder whether to go for broke and finish it off or save a bit for later. I put the bottle back with just the merest droplet in reserve and curse the soldiers for drinking me dry!

I stumble along in gloomy silence clutching my talisman. It's a bloody long way to the middle, I'd forgotten.

'Oooh, Al! Come and see!' Lorna waves her torch in my face and I'm blinded temporarily.

'*Look!* Ronnie ... Lorna... Alan ... 1976!'

I make out our names etched into the stone, still visible after all these years. I can't see Karen's name. At 14, Karen was too young to hang around with us but Ron brought his sister along to show her the tunnel.

'God, if only I knew then what I know now,' Lorna says. 'I'd have kept me legs crossed and never took up smoking again.'

Lorna had her first kid when I was sitting my English 'A' level. She lost touch with the kid's father, a Jamaican who drove the number 79 bus. Two years later, while I was spending all my time drinking in the students' union bar and getting off with girls instead of preparing for teaching practice, she gave birth to twin boys.

'I'll never forget,' Lorna says. 'The twins was crying, Alex was whingeing and I was tearing me hair out. Me mate cum round, took one look at me and went to the shop. She cum back with two dummies, chocolate buttons for Alex and 20 Benson's for me. If only the daft cow had bought me some Galaxy instead!' Lorna's respiratory tract rumbles with mirth.

Karen wanted kids, somehow it never happened. Just as well, I would have been a crap dad.

'Poor Ron,' Lorna traces his name with her finger.

I wasn't surprised when he told me he was going to join the navy. Well, you couldn't imagine him stuck in a factory all day. I'd already left for London but I didn't want Ron going off to the other side of the world! Whenever I thought of home, it was Ron I thought of, not Mom and Dad and Jules. We were like brothers; we'd known each other since he threw a salvo of conkers over the fence at me when we were five. When I went to college, we didn't see each other for months at a time but we always picked up where we left off, the way you do with good mates. We always had a laugh. Night before he went to the Falklands, we got drunk and jumped over all the garden fences on our way home like we had when we were 15.

Lorna ferrets inside her padded jacket and pulls out a long stemmed rose with a bit of straggling fern attached to it, black in the gloom.

'For Ronnie,' she says

'What are you going to do with it?'

'Leave it here on the towpath – by his name.'

The thought of it winds me up. 'Bollocks, who started this fucking crazy idea of leaving flowers to rot at the fucking roadside? What kind of tribute is it?

'What's your problem, Alan?'

'Well, what's the point? You die and that's it. I've never visited the crem or left flowers for the old man. I don't even know where they put his ashes.'

'Well, maybe you should ask your sister.'

I begin to shake. I grip the bottle inside my pocket.

'Well, what shall I do with it, then?'

I snatch the rose and chuck it in the cut. It lands with a soft thwack.

'Christ, Alan.'

I lean over the rail and stare into the soft, inky water illuminated by the silvery reflection of the overhead air vent, gently rippling from the fall of Ronnie's rose. Water drips with an irregular musical plinkety plink. Twenty five years: a long time dead.

When we were ten, Ron saved my life. There was a tip over the road to where we lived and we used to sneak in and mess about. It was just a wasteland. They buried a lot of rubbish there when they were building the M6. It was mine and Ronnie's haven. We had a den. One day we were playing around by a bog. I felt the ground give way beneath my feet, the earth was sucking me in. I remember shouting out 'I'm a gonner' and the next thing I know, there's Ronnie throwing out a plank of wood and I'm grabbing hold of it and he hauls me out of the stinking slurry. If Ron hadn't kept his head, I could've died that day.

'Maggie Thatcher was on the news yesterday making a speech about the Falklands, did you see it?' Lorna says.

I grunt a negative response and watch the rose slide into some weed. A bloated corpse looms on the surface of the canal. I am paralysed with terror until I realise it's a plastic bag.

'It meks you wonder if it was all worth it.' Lorna gives the handrail a sharp tap and wanders off, swinging the sallow beam over the walls and ceiling.

Ron was on the Sheffield when it was hit by an Exocet missile. He stayed at his post with the team trying to get the ship's computers back on so she could defend herself but, unknown to them, the attacking planes had long since fled. I drain the last precious dregs from the bottle and throw it into the canal. I miss the plastic bag.

Lorna whispers, 'what was that plop?'

'A rat, maybe.'

'Alan, don't piss about.' Lorna was petrified of rats. It was her main objection to going down the tunnel in the first place. She'd been brave to overcome her fear – brave or bloody minded – as I said she never liked Ron to get one over on her.

'It was only me disposing of the empties.'

'Fucking hell, Al!'

We walk in silence. I think Lorna's mad with me or maybe she's thinking about Ron and what might have been.

Thank Christ, it's the end! We don't need the torch anymore. We walk through the gloaming and out of the tunnel, blinking like miners at the end of a shift. It's cloudy but bright as if the sun is trying to break through.

'I got suspended,' I say.

'Why?' Lorna sucks on a cigarette as if her life depends on it. I notice worry lines etched into her forehead. Her eyes are slightly bloodshot. There are grey streaks in her pale hair.

'I pushed a girl over in class. It was an accident but she said I did it on purpose. I just wanted her out of the way – I was trying to get to the toilets.'

'You were pissed!'

'I was sick. She was in the way, so I nudged her aside and puked up in the bin – at least, I aimed for the bin – I don't really remember much about it.'

As if - the whole excruciating scene replays constantly in my head: the class in uproar - teenagers screaming in disgust and delight, the girl shrieking, fists banging on desks, feet drumming on the concrete floor - me retching. It was an extraordinary sound, like a drop forge running out of control. Crap school, zero discipline. It didn't take much to get the kids going at the best of times, third generation on the dole. Half of them had never been more than two miles up the road out of their enclave. The little bastards were inbred to the point of retardation and behaved as if they were all high on crack. It was only a matter of time before one of them pulled a knife on me – or a gun. I'd been practically teetotal when I started at that school – well, I was off Scotch, at any rate.

'I didn't mean to knock her over.'

Lorna squints at me through her smoke haze. I know what she's thinking. I hadn't meant to push Karen down the stairs either. It was an accident for Christ sake.

'So, what's going to happen?'

'They'll do an investigation and I'll get the sack, I suppose.'

'Don't be daft, Al. They'll send you to Occupational Health.'

'They already did, I didn't make the appointments.' Hung over and couldn't be arsed, more like. 'So I'll definitely get the boot.'

I giggle and Lorna frowns – must think I'm off my rocker.

'You're a stupid sod!' Lorna sounds exasperated but she pats my shoulder, my eyes fill up. I blow my nose while she stares into the gloomy portal and smokes another fag, taking short, anxious puffs. I don't think I can make it to the Dry Dock after all, neither does Lorna.

'Do you want to stay here and I'll goo and get the car?'

Great idea! While I'm waiting, I could find a pub or shop, sink a quick pint to steady my nerves and stop this ridiculous shaking. But I shouldn't let her go on her own, she's scared. I hesitate too long.

'I'll tek that as a yes!'

Lorna sets off at a brisk pace like a woman with something to prove. I see her falter as the darkness shrinks round her. She fumbles for her torch and I wonder how far she'll get before she returns defeated. She could panic deep inside and fall over the rail into the Stygian waters to disappear forever. Or perhaps she'll meet a serial killer coming the other way! Calling her name, I stumble after, clutching the handrail.

'I hate teaching. It's like a fucking production line and yet all the goods turn out faulty.'

'And when you've finished it's over to people like me. You're not the only one with a stressful job, Alan. You want to sort yourself out. Get some help.'

I went through this time and again with Karen.

'I'm going to quit, Karen. I really mean it.'

'That's what you said last time.'

I always start with good intentions but then something happens, I get a really shit class I can't control and on the way home I go to the pub just for a quick one and three hours later they're putting me in a taxi. Karen was always so *disappointed* and *hurt* as if it was something I'd done on purpose to upset her.

'Alan, you *promised*!'

'You know what *really* pisses me off, Karen? Your miserable face! For fuck's sake cheer up! Have a drink.'

It was a relief when she packed her bags and left; haven't seen her for years.

I clutch the handrail. I'm sweating and shaking. My mouth is dry, my heart is hammering. I feel an almost irresistible compulsion to jump in the cut.

'It's a panic attack,' Lorna says. 'Tek some deep breaths.'

I stare into the abyss. Twenty-five years was a long time dead. I try to imagine all the great things Ron might have achieved if he'd lived.

'It should have been me not Ron! I've wasted my life!'

'Stop feeling sorry for yourself!'

I wonder if she speaks like that to her patients. Maybe it's me. People are sympathetic at first then they don't want to know.

There's a light in the distance. Not the bright white light at the end of the tunnel, but a soft, hazy, yellowy light, accompanied by a dull, throbbing noise, gradually getting louder. We can't make it out at first but as the light draws near we realise a narrow boat is navigating the tunnel. On board, a man calls gruffly in response to Lorna's salutation. There's something appealing about this solitary travelling man. Maybe I should try it, give me space and time to get my head together. I must stop drinking.

'Here comes another one,' says Lorna, as the sound of laughter and friendly banter bounce off the tunnel walls and a boat full of exuberant youths waving beer cans rumbles past.

'I wonder if that pub's still there, the one with a bar that looks like a narrow boat.'

'Hope so, I need the loo.'

We emerge from the tunnel back where we started to find the clouds are breaking up. Three goats are grazing in a paddock near the pub and a couple of dusty hens scratch about. It's strange to think we're in the urban sprawl. Lorna clicks her tongue to a friendly goat but its cloven feet and strange eyes look devilish to me as it ambles to the fence. Lorna pushes grass through the chicken wire while I hop about.

'C'mon, Lor, I thought you were desperate!'

The pub is much as I remember, except it's crammed with canal heritage paraphernalia. Someone's gone mad painting bargee roses and scrolls on everything. A trio of blokes in overalls and paint splattered boots eat vast meat pies, chips and mushy peas. An old woman sits alone with a half polishing spoons.

'I'm dying for a wee,' Lorna shimmies past.

'What do you want, Lor?'

'Apple and Mango J20 and sausage, egg and chips – I'm starving!'

I buy a J20 and a pint. I drink the pint whilst I place an order with the cheery bar man for sausage, egg and chips and a cheese sandwich, then I buy another pint. It's good stuff – real ale. I tell myself I'll stick to beer from now on and lay off the Scotch.

'Just for a minute there, Al, I didn't think you were gooing to mek it!' Lorna returns and collapses next to me, lighting a fag. There's a beer mat on the table, advertising the imminent smoking ban. 'Christ, I won't be able to do this much longer!'

'I couldn't let you walk through the tunnel on your own.' I've nearly finished the second pint. Lorna's barely touched her soft drink.

'Fuck that,' says Lorna, with a rasp. 'I'd have called a taxi.'

The cheese sandwich arrives and I haven't got the stomach for it so I fetch another pint. Lorna demolishes the sausage, egg and chips, lights another fag, leans back with a contented sigh and fiddles with the beer mat.

'When the ban comes in I'm giving up fags.'

We laugh. The bar man whistles through his teeth as he reads his *Sun*. The workmen guffaw at some banter. The sunlight, streaming through the window, flashes off the old biddy's spoons. My spirits lift. I'm almost cheerful. I call to the old biddy and make her laugh by cracking a pathetic joke about playing the spoons. I smoke one of Lorna's fags. When I go to the gents, I stop to chat to the workmen about the forthcoming local derby, Villa versus the Blues. We're all Villa fans! I insist on buying them each a half - they joke they won't have pints because they're roofers and can't risk sliding off any gables! I flirt with the old girl and persuade her to have one on me. I have another pint whilst Lorna checks her voicemail.

As we leave, the sun's beating down. Too late, I realise I forgot to drink a toast to Ron! Distraught, I want to go back to the pub but Lorna has to pick up her grandkids. We toil up the hill to the car sweating - unlike that day in 1976, when the savage wind whipped icy rain into our faces and our waterlogged flared jeans wrapped around our legs as we battled through thistles and billowing waist high grass beneath hissing pylons. We didn't care. We were young and we thought we could do anything. Ron was going to join the marines and see the world, Lorna would be a holiday rep in Majorca and I was Mr Harrison's star pupil, a working class lad on track for university. The old, ragged horses tethered on the hillside, wind lashed monuments to suffering, turned their mournful heads as gargantuan Ron bellowed at the ill wind, 'Ooh, the bastard wind!'

His Black Country voice carries to me across the decades - young, invincible - spitting in the eye of the devil and I'm overcome with grief for me and Ron and Lorna too. We didn't ask much but our dreams came to nothing! Oh, how I wish the bastard wind would come and blast the years away! I feel so down! When I get on the train, I'll have a large Scotch, cheer myself up.

Morgan's Bay

Lucy Fussell

From the field, the path down to the beach was hardly visible, just a little dip in the rough grass before the land dropped away to the sea. The wind was catching the seed heads of the grass, making them dance in the sunshine. Clumps of thrift and wild thyme, dark green and pink, clung to the thin soil.

When we got to the edge, it became clear where the path led to the shore. It was the only sloping place in a huddled line of black rocks that edged the sand. Once down there, our feet sank into the dry softness and we kicked off our shoes to feel its warmth between our toes. That first touch of summer, more than anything, made my shoulders relax and my stride lengthen. I stopped, turned my face to the sky and closed my eyes.

Leaving David had been hard. Ten years and a small child were stronger ties than all his rage could break. Until fear shook me loose and I left, with only Morgan and my books.

When I opened my eyes again, Morgan had dropped his bags a little way along the beach and was racing headlong for the white-tipped blueness; arms wide and welcoming, his pale stick-legs propelling him forward, his feet pounding the damper, tide-left sand until diamonds of salty water sprayed up around him and slowed him to a breathless, high-stepping walk. Even from so far back, I could tell that his eyes were shining and he was shouting his hellos to the sea. I dropped my bags beside his and ran to join him in the waves.

The darkness of the past drained into the shallow pools my feet left.

The Hawk

Lucy Fussell

The sun started to warm the back of the young man's neck and he shifted slightly into a patch of shade. No point getting too hot, it was going to be a long day and it wouldn't be easy to keep comfortable.

He rested his arm on the low wall round the roof's edge and gazed at the people below him. Sometimes they might look like ants from this height, their colours dark and muted, but today, in this sun-drenched city, they looked like brightly-coloured fish, swimming in and out of the coral-reef shadows of the buildings; here and there a shoal of them interrupting the flow of traffic. Sounds reached him late, oddly loud, like a film run in slow motion, a confused mixture of people and cars.

Where were they all going? Work? Friends? A day's shopping? All pouring out of their dark little hideaways, eager to leave the sanctuary of home for the noise and danger of the outside world, or their own little part of it, mostly not even aware that there are other ways of living, other ways of thinking.

He stretched and rubbed the back of his neck, screwing his eyes up tight, then blinking, as if trying to clear his vision. Moving his shoulders to ease the tension in them, he reached into the bag beside him for the flask of cold water.

Cool water.

As it poured down the young man's throat, images of home floated into his consciousness: rain on the house across the street; his mother laughing as she washed his sister's hair; grandmother telling one of her endlessly evolving stories as she poured drinks for the children; his sister, ten years old, biting her lip in an effort to stop a single drop from spilling out of an enormous bowl she was carrying; himself, Hanif, playing with the other boys, leaping off a diving board into the pool, huge fountains bursting upwards; grandfather's tears, bitter and hot, as they always are for the death of a child. *It should not happen that the young die before the old.*

Anger clenched Hanif's chest. Tears started to blur his vision. He put down the flask, breathed deeply and concentrated on the warm breeze that stroked his cheek. He listened to the sounds around him, separating them into their component parts, waiting for his breathing to return to normal. The fury and grief that had brought him to this place were now his enemies. He must understand them and contain them. He must keep his senses sharp. He could hear the sounds of the traffic and somewhere the throb of a helicopter. He looked for it across the deep blue of the sky, but it was not close enough to cause him anxiety, and he watched as the sun's reflection flashed off its retreating side

Helicopters had been a constant presence in his life for as long as he could remember. As a child in Yorkshire, he had wondered what it must be like to be able to hover above the world, like a hawk looking down at the people below, some of them going about their daily business, hardly aware of the huge machine, held in the air, some of them shading their eyes to gaze up at it. He had imagined himself magically transported to its interior, waving and calling to his friends, perhaps dropping flour on his sister, Abir, so that she would look all around, covered in white, wondering where it had come from. The thought made him smile even now, but it brought memories of other helicopters that were much less innocent, with guns fixed to their sides, piloted by men who had only hatred for his country and his people, who came without warning and fired missiles into the homes of his neighbours. He could still hear the screams of the injured and the terrified, but what weighed most on his heart was the silence of the dead.

The numbness he'd felt at first confused him. It must be a terrible person who could not feel sadness for people so close to his family. He listened to the wailing of his mother and grandmother, saw his sister's tears, heard his father's serious voice, and knew that life had changed. He'd wanted to scream at them all that they were wrong, that if he couldn't race down the street laughing with his friend, then things would keep on being wrong, as if the sadness caused the wrongness. But instead he just listened and watched, waiting for the time when his parents would allow him to go outside on his own again.

It didn't take long before he found ways to meet up with the other boys to play football or saunter through the streets to the park and the old swimming pool. Although his mother was more anxious and cross, she let him go, saying that, whatever happened, it would be God's will. He remembered that time, after the first attack, as a time of quiet. People salvaged what they could from the damaged houses, but he didn't go in. He thought he saw, or heard, the ghosts of the neighbours' children too often to want to go looking for them. He spent as much time as he could outdoors, or in the dappled sunlight of the pool.

Hanif tried to remember if he had been aware in those days of what was happening in the wider world, or even in England, but he could only be sure that this was the beginning of his enmity. There must have been conversations between the adults in the house about what was going on around them, but he could only recall the build up of tension, the crackle of gunfire in the night and the tanks looming at the side of the road. Then the soldiers came. They were vindictive, shouting words he did not understand, lashing out at anyone in their way. He remembered the feeling of helpless indignation as they took his father and grandfather, bullying them out of the house and into a van, like dogs. It felt like the world had lost its cohesion.

The next day, he went with his friends to hurl stones and curses at the tanks. They were just boys with pebbles, venting their anger, not a danger to the soldiers. Why was it then, that the soldiers opened fire? He would never understand it. He could never knowingly cause the death of a child, no matter who its parents were. On that day, when he saw his best friend, Patrick, lying very still in the road, he could not understand what he was seeing. It made no sense. The moments it took him to turn and run almost cost him his life.

The weeks following were a confusion of outbursts and nightmares in his memory. He stayed close to home and helped his mother to pack as much as she could: getting ready to leave as soon as his father should be released. Grandfather was home in a few days, but would not speak about what had happened to him in front of the children. He seemed very old and fragile, and when his son walked into the house, he held him for a long time.

The journey to the refugee camp was not like earlier journeys to the seaside. There was no laughter or excitement. It was hot and uncomfortable and anxious. The car was loaded with belongings and he and his sister sat squeezed in-between them. Every time they were stopped, he could see the tension in his mother's back, every time they moved off, he had to check behind so he could tell his father that their grandparents had come through the checkpoint safely. When they arrived though, he remembered the warm welcome from family friends, and the feeling that maybe this would be like a holiday after all. Maybe they would have a good time with the friends' children and then go home to find the soldiers and the tanks and the helicopters gone. Maybe he would soon be swimming at the pool again with his friends. From the vantage point of adulthood, Hanif felt irritated by his own stupidity, and a deep longing for those childish hopes.

Life in the camp was cramped and restricted. There was no swimming, no wandering off as he pleased. Food was in short supply and water had to be collected carefully in improvised rain barrels. The concrete shelters were small and crowded together and there were no tree-lined streets or parks to wander in. But everyone was in the same situation, and there were wonderful, crazy games of football in the narrow alleyways. He'd found himself going back to the house often though, to make sure that everyone was still there, listening to grandmother's stories like a small child, offering to help his mother, just so he could be near her.

Hanif, on the rooftop, took another sip of water and a few moments to check his surroundings and his watch. His later memories were more painful, and it had taken a long time before he had been able to face even the disjointed images of his dreams. Once he let them in, the flood of anguish had overwhelmed him.

The soldiers, who had become a more regular and threatening presence in the camp, had been rounding up the older boys, searching them, questioning them and letting them go. If anyone answered back they were bundled into a van and taken away. Sometimes houses were raided and someone's father or uncle was vanished, maybe for a few days, maybe longer. Curfews were ordered, but no one knew when they would happen until they were in force. Many people, old, young, men, women and children were arrested. There was talk of fighting back and guns were hidden in a number of homes. Hanif's father would not allow them in his house; he said they only brought more trouble, that the right way was to talk, to persuade, to tell the rest of the world what was happening to their people. He'd talked to the boy, explained to him that violence is not the same as strength, that there is always a better way to deal with a situation than by killing. Hanif was torn between the dignity of his father's principles and the humiliation of being unlike other families.

But when the helicopter gunships came, and tanks surrounded the camp, no one could believe that talking would make any difference. As shells thudded in, people caught outside ran for the nearest shelter. Rifles were as ineffectual as the boys' stones had been. Hanif had tried to get home, but the alleyways were too dangerous, he was forced to stay where he found himself and wait. It took a long time. The shelling lasted for hours.

He had only a vague memory of the walk back home. Crumpled buildings, a car blown onto its roof, everything covered in white dust. He did not recognise his own area, and asked directions when he was already there. By the rubble that had been his home, his grandfather knelt, rocking back and forth, a thin, high sound coming from his lips. His arms cradled a bundle that had once been Hanif's sister, and tears ran down his face. There was no sign of anyone else.

Neighbours helped to lift the rubble and pull out the bodies of his parents and his grandmother. There were so many dead. They were buried quickly, with little ceremony. The living must come first, and there were many injured. Clearing and rebuilding had to start immediately. Everyone helped. There was no more time for childhood, and very little time for grieving.

The local authority worked at getting people in the world outside to take notice, to understand what was happening to them and to put pressure on the occupying army to stop. But it seemed clear to the younger people that this was not enough, if help had not come by now, it would not come at all. Some of Hanif's friends had got hold of rifles and had started taking pot shots at soldiers. The response came with the sound of rapid gunfire and the smell of burning. His friends' deaths seemed pointless to him.

When the chance came to use his choked-back rage to make a difference, he took it. Three of them left together for the training camp. They travelled cheaply, on false papers, with almost no luggage and with no one else taking responsibility. Grandfather had asked him not to go, but otherwise didn't try to stop him. He said that every man must make his own choice in life and his own peace with God. The young man would not forget the old man's face.

Training was hard, but it gave him a sense of purpose and, after a while, confidence in his own physical and mental strength. He learnt to understand his memories and his anguish. He felt clear about the future and his own part in it. He learnt how to use guns, rocket launchers, and explosives. He learnt how to use his surroundings so that he could move almost invisibly through any environment. And he learnt how far he could manage to live without relying on others.

While he was at the camp, trainees came and went. He read about some of them in news reports and, although he could sympathise with their reasons, was horrified that innocent lives were destroyed by what they did. He was horrified too by a report about the general who had ordered the destruction of his home and family. This man had told his own government,

'The aim is to increase the number of losses on the other side. Only after they have been battered will we be able to conduct talks.'

Hanif thought of his mother, his father, his grandmother and his sister, crushed under the rubble of their shelter, and he made his choice. His weapon would be accurate and would strike at only those who had given the orders. He chose a Nighthawk rifle, dark, powerful, and as precise as the person firing it.

He felt the cool rigidity of the wall at his back. His fingertips stroked the roughness of the concrete roof, reminding him of warm evenings under the stars, eating and talking with his parents and grandparents, drifting in and out of sleep, not fully understanding the adult conversation, but knowing that he was safe with them. Knowing that whatever happened their strength would hold him. He could still feel their strength, even through the curtain of death. He heard them in his heart. He saw his father's image for a moment in the shadows, smiling a blessing, and so much more real than the brightly coloured people below.

He looked down at the street again. It seemed even busier,

and the traffic moved slowly, cars, vans and lorries jostled for position. In the distance Hanif thought he saw the car he had been waiting for, dark and sleek. He took the binoculars from the side pocket of his bag, and felt an increase in his heartbeat, but waited and watched, not moving until he was sure. A slight breeze lifted the little flag on the car's bonnet, and then he knew. As he put his hand on the rifle, the training of the past year took over and he moved automatically, setting up the gun, checking the sight then flexing his shoulders and fingers, before settling behind his weapon and readying himself for the shot.

As the car pulled up outside the building almost opposite him, doors opened and a tall man, familiar from many TV and newspaper photographs, was ushered out. Hanif curled his fingers round the trigger and drew them tight. The Nighthawk spat out its revenge.

Vehicles

Dave Ewer

'What d'ya think, Spider?'

I almost asked for a fag, before remembering I'd packed in, then limped round the motor giving it the once over, keeping my good eye trained on Laurie. 'Mud - nearside rear wheel arch.' I pointed a gloved finger. Apart from that, the vehicle, a black two year old sedan with a 3.5 V6 supercharged petrol engine was clean, classy and perfect for springing our Mikey. My hip was hurting like hell, so I dropped a couple of black and white painkillers. 'Mo's sorted it?'

Laurie nodded, polishing.

Mo fixes autos under the railway arches. I'm like family. This is one of his specials, a mongrel, put together from write-offs. After welding, filling and spraying, it looks almost as good as new. Of course, appearances can be deceptive.

'She's beautiful,' said Laurie, like the limo was his girlfriend. 'One last date then wumpf!' he laughed and mimed flicking a lighter. 'Torch the mad cow!'

'And your carbon footprint?' I asked.

'I take my shoes off to drive,' he said, 'so it ain't me boss.'

Laurie wasn't much to look at and could hide in an empty lift. Nobody'd ever seen him eat. Rumour was, he lived, loved and serviced pushbikes on lager alone: a lifestyle choice which contributed to his dismal appearance. It's fair to say the fashion train had never stopped at his station since I'd known him. He'd worn the same clothes for decades; brown boots, check shirt, jeans and tank-top. Other than dirty shoulder-length hair, he was a bang to rights skinhead. But you could trust Laurie when it kicked off.

I caught the time on the car stereo; Dawson was due. Folk said he was loco because back home his mama bashed his head with a broom to drive out the devil. Knowing her, you'd well believe it. She'd spent her life confronting evil, mostly in her husband who was proper bad; an enforcer for some northern gang, but well dead now. Word is, he beat his son until he was big enough to fight back. Now Dawson's not the kind of person you want around most of the time - it's bad for business – but we needed his help to release our Mikey. I wouldn't be begging him mind; it was strictly cash in big black hand.

Painkillers kick in quickly on an empty stomach. I found myself leaning against last year's tyre manufacturers' calendar, watching Laurie slide from the driver's seat, squint through the peep-hole, then whisper, 'Fuck, an eclipse!'

Dawson appeared in wrap-around sunglasses, black trilby and a raincoat: he could have been a spook protecting the president. I'd forgotten how big he was in the flesh. Y'know that local comedian - the one on the mint advert – imagine him, swinging a cricket bat about his head; that's how I remembered Crazy Nate – en route to battle the next estate. Luckily for the lads in our neighbourhood, Nathaniel Clarence (best not mention the middle name to his face) Dawson's family moved into our street. He'd been our Mikey's best mucker, and ran in the same gang. Happily, Nathaniel wasn't carrying a weapon that day, but humping the mother of all sacks; stuffed full with helmets, vests and overalls, cones, lamps, fluorescent tape and cables. His weightlifter's poise displayed when he squatted and gently lowered his burden to the concrete. Ho-ho-ho.

I waited while Dawson wiped each brow with a great white handkerchief, then slapped my doll-like palm in his big black paw. Still holding my hand, he looked me up and down and said, 'What's the plan, Prof?' He nodded towards the street. 'Scooterboys are ready.'

I'm a dealer, shifting stuff to earn a few bob; evading the law by fronting a bike shop known as *Spider's Cycles*, but Nate still called me *Professor*. He'd landed in our manor from heaven and we were close at school. I did his homework in exchange for cassettes of classic tunes. He'd have me say, 'Reading, writing and arithmetic', then double up at my petite voice. I took him back to our house once: Mum said, 'What do they eat?' 'You ask,' I said, 'I'll translate.' After hysterical laughter, we had baked beans.

Fifteen years passed quickly. We'd meet at gigs and I'd hear of him flattening somebody or trashing a pub. I fenced things for him, but we never worked together. Lately, people said he'd found religion, but I didn't buy that; he looked more criminal than clerical to me - Die Hard not Jihad. Facts were, Dawson was the best man for this job, and wanted in the moment he'd known the score.

I sent Laurie for chocolates and espresso, leaving us to reminisce about the Ringroad Boys and old friends.

'My sister Josephine still harbours feelings for you,' he said.

Shit, I'd forgotten Jo - as beautiful as Nathaniel was big, and doubly dangerous. Call me over cautious, but becoming romantically involved with any of Nate's relatives never seemed a sensible option. Luckily Laurie returned with drinks and we began to discuss the caper. Gulping coffee, I necked two of the anti-depressants I'd started on after mum died.

'Our Mikey's appeal's been knocked back,' I said to Nathaniel. 'He can't handle more bird so we've hatched a plan. He's put his hand up to a few robberies and the law's swallowed his story. Mickey's being delivered to crown court for sentencing this morning: we'll intercept the truck and lighten their load.'

'Every little helps,' agreed Nate. 'What route they taking to court?'

Laurie produced the map, before putting a cigarette between his thin lips. Out of habit, my hand reached for the packet but I somehow stopped myself and said, 'Give us what you've got, Laurie.'

Dawson suddenly pipes up, 'Yes sir, step forward Mister Laurie Ashanti – sing for your supper.' Nate considered Laurie a dead ringer for reggae star Manno Ashanti. Apart from ginger hair and vastly differing body types they could have been brothers. But Laurie stiffened, hating having the piss taken out of him.

'Nate's only joking,' I said and playfully punched Dawson's shoulder while raising my eyebrows as if to say, *Come on boys!* However, neither man smiled and I began to worry whether they could work together. 'Remember guys,' I said. 'Today's about Mikey – I'm all for a bit of sledging, but this is serious. He's already served three, and looking at another five before being considered for parole. Losing the appeal's crushed him - threatened he'd top himself last visit.'

'Been following the vans for over a fortnight,' Laurie muttered, eyes on the map. 'They switch between two routes. Expected 'em to be smarter, but it's all about this,' he said, rubbing his fingers together. 'Since privatisation, they take the shortest route.'

'Figures,' grunted Nathaniel nodding. 'We'll pick a prime place to set up - gotta be spot-on for the sharp exit as well.'

While they discussed locations, I studied the samples my contact had dropped off the night before, expecting feedback from me within the week. These designer substances were so new they didn't have street names: the big bosses apparently hoping the punters would come up with something catchy. 'I mean,' he'd said, counting out five innocent-looking white tablets with small symbols imprinted on one side, 'who calls drugs by their chemical formulas?'

The caffeine had sharpened me up and I couldn't feel my hip. Nate and Laurie were still arguing about tram termini and feeder lanes as I placed the tablets on my gloved palm. I saw an eye on the first and guessed a light bulb on the next. The third was easy; an arrow, but pointing where? The fourth held a hand and the last featured an airliner. I was relieved to see Laurie smiling, so put my thumb up, grinned back, then swallowed the pill with the plane. I could hardly sell the shit to my people without describing its effects and besides, my spirits needed lifting.

'Don't worry,' said Nathaniel. 'We're doing all we can.'

Trouble was, I'd felt responsible for Mikey since we were kids. We were both tearaways, yet he always got caught. If we were chased and split at a fork in the road, Old Bill or the other gang would always follow him. And Mikey could never hold on to money. I set him up with all manner of schemes. Gave him a briefcase of drugs once, complete with scales, bags, phone numbers of people waiting to score, everything really: fortnight later, got a call, 'Your brother's in the nuthouse'. He'd done all the gear and was properly fucked up. I soon forgave him, because we all lose it occasionally. Just look at me.

'Professor!'

I came to, realizing the lads had reached a conclusion.

'You're not coming with us, Spider,' said Laurie, avoiding eye contact.

'My man and me have worked out where we're going to make our play. And you,' Nate said pointing two black pudding fingers, 'I'm sorry to say, are the individual our friends in blue will most expect to be involved. So you must take no obvious further part.' He could see I was disappointed and added, 'Hold your horses, Professor. Your role's to relay information on the whereabouts of your kid and his chauffeurs to the road workers,' He gestured to Laurie and himself. 'And we need to avoid leaving a telephone trail for the law. Nowadays, it's phones what get you bust. So put your skates on, visit the big supermarket and stroll round like you own the place, and ensure you get caught on the security cameras. That's your alibi, innit? Buy a couple of disposable mobiles – disposable – get me? You can sling 'em after.' He nodded his head and winked. 'Then go and sit in the coffee shop and enjoy a quiet cuppa.' He gave me some numbers on a piece of paper. 'Ring me when you get to the cafe.' Then looking at me closely, like I was shining or something, he said softly, 'You okay?'

'Great, why?'

'You're pale.'

'Of course I'm pale, I've always been pale – our Mikey's pale and all my cousins are pale,' I said. 'The Webster's are a pale family.'

I felt talkative and a little lightheaded, but unusually calm. I argued, but it was useless – they wouldn't take me with them. After loading Nate's van, Laurie followed him in the mongrel motor. I locked the unit and strolled, only slightly unsteadily, to my little silver two-seater.

I'd shut the door and was sitting trying to remember how to drive, when I realised something was missing: music. I pressed a button and an orchestral concerto crashed against the shore of my already-heightened senses, utterly overwhelming all notions of self, just as a breaking wave obliterates yesterday's footprints. I was a magnificent eagle, soaring aloft and far beyond the moonlit, snow-capped, rocky peaks; gliding effortlessly over green, green grass, then circling, weightless, serene, above vast deciduous forests, before plunging directly down, dropping dead as stone, to pluck with plash, and grasp, with talons sharp, the splashing, thrashing fish, from deep beneath the surface of some storming tropical sea. I was understandably reluctant to return to as mundane an activity as driving, then remembered our Mikey, so started the car. The throb of the engine harmonised with the music, and the scherzo section spurred me on. I considered myself in a race, and fully intended to win.

In retrospect, it's obvious the new drug had kicked in. I've this memory of piloting a powerful motorboat through the pedestrian precinct and across High Street, before roaring round the council buildings and finally plunging headlong into the gaping maw of a fearsome subterranean monster, (probably an underground car park). I don't remember the rest of the journey to the supermarket, but somehow made it alive.

At 8.30 the retail park was empty so finding a space was easy, but I was wary of alighting from the roadster, thinking myself still at sea. I had to drop my keys from the window before having the bottle to open the door. I studied the four remaining pills before pushing the arrow to one side, leaving an eye, the hand and light bulb. I could see well enough so saved the eye for later. I swallowed the light bulb, pocketing the others, reasoning I was bound to need a hand sometime.

The sun, brilliant behind the buildings, was pale and lacking in warmth. Shops were decorated for the holiday period, and little lights winked at me from the shadows. I winked back at a few then aimed myself at what I hoped was the entrance. Closing my eyes, I could hear carols playing close-by and for a moment almost believed in the mystery of the season. Upon opening them again, the shoppers' faces gave me a right surprise. Everybody's features were exaggerated; eyes were impossibly bright and bulging, noses longer, lips redder and teeth sharper – it made me think of illustrations for old fairy stories. There were mirrors on the pillars but I was afraid to look at myself. Leaning on a trolley, I toured the aisles trying to remember why I'd come. My sense of smell being extremely acute, the vegetable section and bread and cakes were a delight, but I avoided the cleaning products and pet foods. Each shopper had a distinct odour. I realized something about dogs that morning.

While watching a girl with unfeasibly long ear lobes using a mobile I remembered my instructions. Everything became very clear. I made my purchases, then strolled to the cafe. Finding a table adjacent to an electric socket, I connected my new telephones, and called a number.

'Laurie's done one,' growled Dawson. 'I'm gonna break him like a cheap pen...'

'Why, what's happened?' I asked. However, my mind was working so quickly I answered the question before Nate. 'Manno Ashanti's new single *Let Go!* came on the radio and you argued.'

'How d'ya know?' Nate said, tough manner forgotten

momentarily.

'Call it intuition,' said I, enjoying his surprise. 'Where'd he jump ship?'

'The old shopping centre.'

He'll be in the saloon of the shitty little boozer round the back – the Wheatsheaf,' I said. 'So please turn round, pick him up gently and remind him this is for our Mikey.'

I rang the other number, while absentmindedly counting the metal lightshades hanging from the roof of the cavernous retail cathedral then multiplying the total by the combined wattage of the lamps. Nate's mate answered; they were following Mikey's wagon from a discreet distance, now crossing the estate where we'd once lived.

I pictured myself looking through the windows of the van and wondered how Mikey would be feeling, seeing these places again. The oak he monkeyed about on's been cut down, but most of the houses in the lane have hardly changed. Some are privately owned - he'll glimpse porches and double glazing, and maybe see the sun shimmer off new roof tiles. Our Mikey's always been radical and can't stand selfish bastards who bought council houses. His soulmate Mary's family lived in the next road. So he'll be reliving the run-ins he had with her father, a wide bloke, fag in mouth, mad hair and a stained vest. The old fella'd been a miner, and always seemed startled by daylight as if just up from the pit.

A store employee, wheezing behind slipper eyebrows, began wiping my table. His breathing reminded me why I'd given up cigarettes. I smiled, handed him a couple of coins then swallowed the rest of my pills, except for the one with the arrow.

There were two boffin-types messing about with books and pamphlets on the next table. I couldn't help overhear their conversation. The bald bloke with the glasses said, 'Nothing spiritual about it – simply an excuse to sell rubbish.'

His partner, a woman, thirtyish, slim and very sure of

herself, said, 'Correct, Neville: another small step towards the commodification of everything.' She shuffled her folders and sipped coffee. Her make-up was perfect. I examined the remaining tablet. It looked so lonely; sympathy got the better of me, and I swilled it down with the last of my latte. En route to the loos, I casually knocked their paperwork off the table, trying hard not to snigger as sheets see-sawed to the sticky floor. If there's one thing I can't stand, it's a stuck up bitch.

I saw my reflection in the lavatory mirror and turned to face myself. I was pale, but black nonetheless. I'd been in denial for too long. Now I could see only a person looking back. Understanding grew - my body was a vehicle for the consciousness residing within. I spotted some graffiti on the wall; nicely written but nonsense. It read, 'Sic transit', and was signed, 'Gloria Mundi'. I've never heard of her – she certainly wasn't local. Unfortunately someone came into the toilet and the moment passed so I washed my hands and left.

Back at the table I heard several beeps but couldn't locate their source. I gazed around; the café was full, and people's faces were still far too freaky. I remembered the mobiles - it was a text message from Nathaniel, 'Lri bk. Rdy. Uok?'

I texted back, 'Me ok. Mky on way, ta x.'

I didn't need to close my eyes to see our Mikey passing the entrance to the garages and the small park with the playground. He was bullied when I wasn't there. I remembered us climbing into the allotments when the owners had gone. We all stole but he often got caught. We'd pick rhubarb and kids who lived closest would fetch sugar. Mikey will be tasting it now, I thought; the contrasting flavours of the crisp red stems and the granulated sugar. My imagination took over and the bitter taste grew and grew in my mouth. I waited till nobody was watching then spat on the floor between my legs. It didn't help.

A phone rang. I answered and a boy on the back of a scooter said, 'The coach's just passed in front of a two storey brick-fronted building and behind what looks like the council depot. 'Hang on,' he said, 'I can see a sign - it says *Local Business Centre*.'

Used to be the dole office; Mikey's former haunt. I couldn't remember when it changed use; I should know; he worked there for years.

Nate rang. 'We're gonna whack 'em in the underpass.'

'Underpants?'

'Underpass, in the underpass! You sure everything's right Professor?'

'Fine,' I replied, moving my fingers in an intricate pattern. 'It's noisy here.'

In truth, I felt like dancing and sang every word as Manno Ashanti's latest hit played from hidden speakers. '*If you love somebody – let them go, just let them go*!' I thought about Laurie and Nate on the road and focused on Mikey in that prison transport.

Suddenly I could see him; it didn't feel like imagination, but an actual vision of my brother. I was so moved, I called his name. To my great surprise he turned his face towards where the imagined sound came from, but couldn't see me. I repeated his name with more urgency. He jumped and said, 'Victoria – can it really be you? My sister; I thought I heard your voice. Surely I'm losing my mind?'

'No, you're not,' I said quietly. 'I'm talking telepathically. Don't speak; somebody'll hear you – just listen. Nate and Laurie are waiting along the route. They've set up temporary traffic lights that'll stop the van. Laurie's got a radio jammer, so the guards can't call for assistance.'

The van with our Mikey must have passed a burger restaurant because I could smell the fat as it oozed through the air vents.

'Nate's got a Santa suit,' I said, wondering why my voice sounded slurred. 'Laurie'll be dressed as a reindeer. When you stop, Nathaniel will push a jack under the front wheels, lift the van, walk round and cut you free with a special saw. Laurie will drive the getaway and you'll be gone in seconds. I've organized a passport and ferry tickets for you and Mary...'

Without warning the experience ended and my awareness swung back to the cafe. I'd tried to re-focus on the van but couldn't see our Mikey. The nerdy couple on the next table were staring at me, so I glared back and they quickly turned away. I remembered what the woman had said about the commodification of everything, and was starting to understand when my eyes became heavy and I had to rest my head on my arms. Realization dawned: I shouldn't have taken the tablet with the arrow. It was pointing down. It was a downer. I thought about my body again, and realized we were all a mixture of male and female, black and white – a bit of everything really - just like one of Mo's mongrel motors.

Then I fell asleep.

The Side that He Captured

Fiona Joseph

Felicity was trying to pacify an old chap in a state about his overdue book when Roger, the senior librarian, asked her if she would mind sitting for him one of these days.

'Photography's a little hobby of mine,' Roger said.

Felicity watched the old man's filthy raincoat as he shuffled off through the revolving door. Had Roger not been hovering she'd have let him off the fine.

'And I'm always looking for new subjects.'

She counted the eighty pence, all tens and coppers, into the till. 'Sorry, Roger, what did you say?' He stated the favour once more, then outlined the terms rapidly as if she'd already given her agreement. There would be no exchange of money on either side and he would provide her with a full set of prints for her to use as she wished.

'And when you're a world famous *couturiere*,' he pronounced the word as if he'd rehearsed it, 'you'll allow me to photograph all your collections, perhaps.' It was common knowledge amongst the library staff that she made her own clothes, working magical designs out of flea market and charity shop finds.

'Right, you mean like a fashion shoot. Is that what you mean?'

'You wore a rather nice dress at our New Year's do.'

So, nothing sleazy then. That was a relief.

The other girls liked to speculate about Roger. Perhaps it was inevitable given that he was the only male colleague in the library. During the six months she'd worked there it had been rumoured, variously, that he and his wife were naturists, swingers and Christians. Felicity tried to stay out of it, believing they made up half the stuff just for something to talk about.

On alternate Wednesdays it was Felicity's turn on the early morning rota to open up. She snapped the lights on, squinting for a few seconds against the brightness. Then she hung up her winter coat in the coffee room and turned on the tap to fill the water heater, the sound of water belching through the pipes both scary and reassuring in the silence. She went up to the counter, found Magna, their book trolley, still loaded with stock from the previous day and pushed her to the non-fiction section, A to H. She began humming.

She was surprised to hear Roger call out a cheery 'Good morning!'

'Christ, you made me jump,' Felicity said. He moved Magna to one side and stood next to her, speaking as though he were afraid of being overheard.

'The other day, I don't know if you remember me mentioning...' He picked up a bundle of books, and reached to put them on the top shelf. His needlecord jacket was the colour of a toad, and his sleeve slipped to expose his arm.

'The photos? No, I hadn't forgotten.' She spoke to his protruding wrist bone and the surrounding long dark hairs. When Felicity finally turned to look up at him she noticed for the first time the extreme paleness of his blue eyes, set widely in the pallor of his face, both these features somehow at odds with his trapezial jaw. He smelled of shaving foam.

They arranged a time – Friday at seven – and a place, her flat. She started to give him directions.

'I'll find it. Don't worry,' Roger said.

All through break time she kept their agreement at the forefront of her mind as a potential conversation topic, and yet something held her back. Roger hadn't, she recalled, asked her to keep it a secret, but when one of the girls asked Felicity what she was doing on Friday and if she fancied a drink, she fibbed and said she was going to see a film with her flatmate. Much of the talk that morning was about their forthcoming staff appraisals with

Roger the following week. They all affected dread, including Felicity.

'You'll be okay,' one of the girls said. 'He likes you.'

On Friday morning, before leaving for work, she tidied the flat and shopped at the convenience store for pasta twirls, a packet of cheese sauce, and a tin of tuna, the latter just in case he wasn't a vegetarian. Either way, if he arrived expecting supper she could knock something up easily.

These extra tasks made her miss her bus and she arrived twenty minutes late for work. Roger was standing in the doorway, pinning a notice to the board.

'It's really not a problem that you're late. These things happen, even to the best of us.' He spoke in a fulsome manner.

Felicity expected him to confirm their engagement that evening, but he didn't, and the fact loomed between them all day, unmentioned by either, seemingly as tricky to broach as a bereavement.

When she got home Felicity selected the pink organza dress Roger had hinted she should wear. The bodice hung stiffly in the wardrobe, its skirts springing to life as soon as she pulled it out. She lifted the sleeves to smooth them out and was amazed as always by their candyfloss lightness.

She rummaged through the tangle of dangly earrings, bracelets, chokers and necklaces that she kept in a margarine tub, and made a pile of jewellery to match the dress. She applied a double mascara layer and another coating of strawberry red lipstick.

The doorbell rang as soon as her digital clock showed 7.00. Roger stood in the doorway, and she could see that behind him he carried his equipment in a couple of shoulder bags. He held a tripod in his hand.

Straightaway, he scanned the flat as though weighing up the options for lighting. The flatmate put her head round the door, asking, 'Do you need me?' to Felicity.

'Might be best if you left us to it,' Roger answered. 'More relaxed, you know?'

He set his bags on the coffee table then pulled out from his rucksack a red velvet throw, which he draped over the sofa and along the floor.

'May I?' he said, taking a vase and an African wooden sculpture to pin the fabric down behind the sofa. Felicity excused herself to go and make coffee.

'Not for me,' Roger shouted behind her.

In the kitchen Felicity trembled a little, either from nerves or where her skin was starting to cool after her shower. She held onto the worktop to steady herself while she waited for the kettle to boil. When she went back in to the lounge, the wall was blank and she saw that he'd removed the framed animal prints and stacked them neatly in a corner. The tripod was in place.

Roger suggested beginning with some warm-up shots and he chattered all the while, as he began clicking.

'Hey,' he said, looking through his lens. 'Did you hear the story about the two gorgeous sisters preparing for a photo shoot? The photographer's telling them to get ready, only one's a bit deaf, so her sister explains, 'he wants us to stand still so that he can focus.' And the first one says, 'What, the two of us?'' Roger laughed and Felicity realised she was supposed to join in.

Try as she might, she couldn't relax. It was as if she'd put on a face mask that had glued her smile and brow into a fixed, bland expression. His voice was encouraging.

'Perhaps sitting down on the sofa, tilt your head a little, that's it, that's great.'

And then suddenly, she was back in childhood, aged ten or eleven maybe; still the age of innocence. She remembered an uncle who liked to take family pictures with his Polaroid; the way he actually said, *smile for the camera*, a cliché even back then; the fretful, chafing wait as everyone crowded around the print, watching for the picture to appear. His girlfriend found some photographs one day of a young girl, *not even sixteen*. There was an outrage.

'Felicity, you're miles away! Now if you could just raise your arms, place your hands against the wall. That's terrific.'

She held her arms up and through the transparent fabric of her sleeve she could see that it was 7.45pm.

Then at last the session was over.

He refused her offer again of coffee or anything to eat: 'I'll come round one evening next week to show you the photos.'

'You can let me have them at work if you like.'

'I'll come round if it's all the same. Everything's a bit frantic at the library, what with the appraisals and stuff. Plus I like to see people's reaction when they see how I've caught them.'

After Roger had gone she noticed there was a free supplement in the newspaper on portrait photography. She would save it for him. But on Monday morning she looked at the magazine on the worktop and something stopped her putting it in her bag. By the next day it had become stained with tea rings, and so she put it in the magazine rack where it got sandwiched between the pages of *Black Hair and Beauty* magazine.

'I've made you a slide show,' he said, on his second visit, when she came back from her kitchen with coffee. He had set up a data projector to screen the images onto the wall. Felicity could hear his laptop whirring into life. The PowerPoint icon clicked, and there she was. He seemed to have set it up so that each image was projected for about five seconds, before it transitioned to the next slide. The soundtrack was listed at the bottom of the screen: *My Sweet Lady* by John Denver, a song she didn't recognise. She felt him scrutinising her as she watched the images one by one.

Some were good, actually, most were great, where he'd clearly used the right lens and effect to flatter her skin and her figure. These she didn't comment on, not wanting to appear vain. Occasionally, one appeared where her eyes were caught half-shut, or she was way out of focus, and for these she forced a laugh over the music and said 'Look at me!' or 'Oh dear!' Overall, there were a greater number of close-up pictures than she expected.

Part way through the slide show he paused at one of these close-ups. Her skin was the texture of fondant icing, and the jewels of her necklace and sheen of her coiled hair were all refracted into brilliant sparkles. But it wasn't these aspects that he wanted to talk about.

'I must show you this. Look at your philtrum in this one. Did you ever see anything more perfect?'

He must have seen her look of confusion.

'Here.' He got up and stood in front of the projected image, the imprint on his face and hands making him look like a lizard, basking in the sunlight of her. He pointed at the dimple between her nose and upper lip. 'Some people say it's the dent made by the angels when they visit us at birth. They tell us all the knowledge and wisdom of the world, but then put a finger to our lips, saying shush, you mustn't tell anyone else your secrets.'

Felicity felt a shudder pass over her.

'I like to think I've captured a different side to you,' he said. 'Perhaps the side that no one else sees.' She supposed he meant a vulnerability.

Then it came again: memories of sitting in the dark during a family slide show; even darker memories not yet reaching the surface of her consciousness. She wanted him to leave. She didn't even want to see the rest of the pictures, but politeness and duty made her smile and say, perversely, *Let's carry on*, the exact opposite of what she meant.

Roger resumed the slideshow. More poses, but by now Felicity looked on blindly. An image flashed and was gone, in less than a second, only time to compute a body, nude, metal, shiny, a device, head looking over shoulder, an improbability of limbs, bound. The next picture was of her again in the organza dress, seated on the sofa in a demure position.

'Wait! What was that?'

'What?'

'That picture. Go back!' Felicity's voice came out as a shout above the ballad.

'Hey, what's up?'

'You had something. A picture. Go back. Go on.'

Roger scrolled back through the previous images and it was all normal, then he fast clicked right to the end. Felicity's heart was pounding with an emotion she couldn't put a name to. She was aware that he was mentioning a drink sometime and she was answering, *Better not, sorry*. He made her a gift of the photographs in a wallet and told her to ask if she ever needed the negatives to make reprints. She couldn't imagine doing so. Who would want copies? She could imagine the girls at work would love to see them, the gossip would keep their breaktimes going for days, but it would involve too many questions and explanations as to why she hadn't mentioned the photo session before.

As soon as Roger left she looked through the photos rapidly, searching for the image from the slideshow. It wasn't there. She scattered them all over the carpet, mixing up the order, her head throbbing while she sat on her heels. Was there a chance she could have imagined it?

A detail from her past tormented her, wouldn't go away, like a hangnail she kept biting. An uncle, some photographs, her parents speaking in hushed voices, the way that she had known, with a child's instinct for survival, that there was no point asking the adults about him.

Eventually Felicity put the photographs back into the wallet and then in a drawer. She didn't look at them again.

She'd been dreaming of a toy house full of voodoo dolls, and woke up with a racing heart, beating as fast as the beep beep of her alarm clock. Immediately, she thought of Roger's words.

How he'd captured a different side to her. It troubled her, and made her recall what she'd heard about voodoo beliefs, that taking someone's photograph was akin to stealing their soul. She told herself she had no time for dawdling and to get up for work.

Roger seemed in an affable mood in the staff meeting, where they met to discuss the latest footfall targets that the council was trying to impose. It was the day before the appraisals and everyone was keen to chip in with their ideas. Felicity waited for a suitable moment to speak.

'I was thinking about how we could get customer feedback more effectively.' She looked down at the notes she'd scribbled in the margin of her agenda. After the slightest of pauses Roger said, 'Any other thoughts, anybody? Let's go on to the next point then.'

It was as if she hadn't said anything: he'd moved over her as smoothly as a car wheel. Felicity spent the rest of the meeting analysing the checked pattern on his tartan shirt, as if she might also discern a pattern in what had happened.

At break time when she offered to make him a coffee and he blanked her again, her heart began a little fluttering, like she had a bird inside her chest gripped within a fist. One of the girls pulled on her arm and looked at her as if to say *What's going on between you two*? She left her lunch untouched and went out.

Her mobile vibrated in her pocket. He'd sent her a text. Relief. It would be an apology, an explanation perhaps. She read the message, and it stated simply that he wanted to change her appraisal to this afternoon, as he'd had an appointment cancelled, and had a free fifteen minutes to spare. She wrote back to say okay.

'You've had your six-month probationary period,' Roger began, 'and I'm going to recommend we extend it for another three months.' He glanced at his watch.

'Right. Wait. Can I ask why, if I'm allowed to? Have I done

something wrong?'

'Not at all. Just a feeling that you might need more time to settle in, so you're more, um, comfortable, shall we say, with the staff and members of the public.' He was inspecting his files on the table, gazing up through the skylight, towards the door, anywhere, it seemed, other than at her. Finally, he looked right at her and she felt the ugliness of his pale blue eyes. 'It's quite a common thing to happen. Nothing to worry about. No shame involved.'

Somehow she stood up, colour flaming her cheeks, and managed to walk to the door, wanting to shout *this is unfair, it's not me, I'm good at my job and you know it.*

On the way home from work she bought the local paper; it was the edition that contained the Jobs pages. That evening she got rid of the photography supplement, putting it out for recycling. The photographs she shredded, feeding them one by one into the machine: all fondant skin, sparkling jewels and shiny coils. She scrunched the organza dress into a bag ready to go to one of the charity shops, and put the matching jewellery in a pouch which she hooked around the hanger.

She got out her stationery box and sat down to write two letters. The first was a letter of resignation that she began with *Dear Roger*. No, that wasn't right. Best keep it formal. The second was an application for a teaching assistant post. She began to daydream of other career possibilities. A friend had recently gone to teach Mathematics out in a remote village school in Ghana. There would be little risk there of anyone taking her photograph.

Simnel's Yew

Bruce Johns

This was the fourth of Marwick's trees they had seen, and the most distant by far. Lawrence reckoned on a two-hour drive, but not on the stop at a roadside café. The place was too flowery, he said, like a girl's bedroom, and just looking at the cakes made his teeth ache. But Violet insisted on buying something in return for using 'the facilities.'

'There's no need,' he complained. 'They can't stop you having a pee for God's sake. It's the law.'

'You don't know that,' she said, spotting a bluff. 'I'll have one of those delicious-looking muffins. Do you want anything, dear?'

She fished in her handbag and produced a little plastic purse, from which was extracted, first, her door key, then a handful of change. Emptied onto the counter the money looked tarnished and confused, as if unsure of its value. Lawrence's finger worked out what was needed, steering silver coins through the dross of two pence pieces. The girl, her face made plain by boredom, scooped them up without counting.

Lawrence gave out that occasions such as these, and all the other services he had rendered since his mother moved to be near him, came under the heading of duty rather than pleasure. Perhaps he believed it. But since his divorce there was no one else to treat or fuss over, and Violet saw that her frailty and lapses in concentration provided him with an outlet for some of love's minor satisfactions: kindness for its own sake, feeling needed. They now lived within walking distance of each other, both of them in reduced circumstances: he unwillingly, in the terraced house, gloomy with books, that was all his share of the settlement allowed; she, bowing to the inevitable, in a retirement flat peopled with photographs and china figures.

He had given her Marwick's *Guide to Great British Trees* as a moving-in present. It had a serious side despite the lavish photographs, with end notes for the specialist and Latin names for everything. But it catered mainly for popular taste by focusing on single specimens, each with a story to its name as well as great age, size or beauty. Lawrence explained that he could have chosen other books on the same theme, with less science in them and forewords by politicians trying to prove they were human. But this was the original, which scooped all the best examples and didn't talk down to its readers. In fact, Marwick could be said to have started a whole genre. A newspaper was serialising the most shameless of the popularisers and in the process had coined the term 'celebritrees', at which point, Lawrence said, he almost decided on another present entirely.

But Violet had been grateful, keeping it by her bed and reading a page or two each night before falling asleep, mind borne aloft by thoughts of fluttering leaves and dappled sunlight. Her favourites were all deciduous, the old familiars which seemed, with their beauty not dependent on extremes of size or colour, to fit with her idea of Englishness. It was she who suggested visiting the nearest of them, which they did on her birthday. Once accomplished and found to be enjoyable, this excursion was repeated with another of the entries to be found locally, and then a third, the idea forming in both their minds of seeing them all. Neither admitted it, but the project seemed to extend Violet's hold on the future. Her life expectancy was being measured in trees.

That first occasion, the one they started with, was the Thackenham Oak, outstanding in every way, according to the *Guide*: ancient, vast, and solitary in the middle of an old-fashioned village green. Marwick called it Albion's Irminsul, so English it should be sacred – a reference which Lawrence had to explain. In full leaf, the canopy seemed to shelter them from more than the sun. Violet said she felt safe there, and made a dry little noise at the back of the throat as if agreeing with herself. The bark was crusty and cracked, with a bloom of green mould. Young acorns poked from their pale cups, shiny and hopeful. Somewhere in the branches overhead birds' wings slapped and snapped like wet towels being shaken.

This was about a year after Lawrence's divorce, itself following closely upon the highlights of his academic career, the book contract and then promotion to Senior Lecturer in Art History. The three things were connected, of course. As work absorbed more of his time Izzy became restless, then cynical, and finally guarded. Violet, to whom she had grown close after losing her own mother, was the first to guess she had something to hide. By the time Lawrence noticed, it was too late. Izzy left him for someone who, in her own words to Violet during their last heart-to-heart, preferred real nudes to painted ones. It was a bitter joke, but the plurals turned out to be prophetic. The lover soon moved on, his interest in women having a selfish, easily-bored aspect that Lawrence labelled dilettante. It was the worst insult he could manage.

Now that he was alone his work expanded into those parts of the evenings and weekends once occupied by quarrels. His book came out, on allegory and allusion in Venetian art. The planned dedication to Izzy was replaced by one to his mother, but only her initials, so that no one would know. Violet noticed and wavered between disappointment at being second choice and pity for Lawrence, reduced to claiming her for his muse. As a husband he had been remaindered and his book looked destined to go the same way. Sales were confined mainly to universities, a fact which he tried to pass off as a compliment to its style. She looked for it in her local library but their art section was very small.

Their second dip into the *Guide* was the elm at Martingdale. This was singled out as a paragon of its species, but also as something of a rarity, one of the few to escape the ravages of disease. Lawrence said it was a classic bereaved by the absence of comparison, a comment Violet found hard to understand. It stood in a private garden on the edge of town, surrounded by a much newer estate, the suburban setting a disappointment. They had to ring the doorbell and ask permission. This was granted by the woman of the house, a pale-faced dowager not much younger than Violet herself, with pencilled eyebrows and a smoker's growl. She seemed vexed by her tree's fame and after croaking her agreement shut the door in their faces. They went through a side gate, as instructed, and found themselves in a formal lay-out of flower-beds and paths. The elm stood at the far end of an elegant lawn, whose perfection made walking on it feel like trespass. They had to dodge the sprinklers, Lawrence joining in Violet's laughter. The tree towered over the gabled roof, and swelled outwards from near the base in a way that was, to her eyes, graceful and feminine – and also familiar, a visual memory from childhood, perhaps, the imprint on her mind of walks, games and other idylls long forgotten. Lawrence, book in hand, insisted on reading out technical terms such as petiole and pedicle, which she knew meant nothing to him. This was his kind of language, though, and she listened patiently while rubbing a leaf between her fingers. How rough it was on one side, and on the other so smooth. She didn't know the reason for this, or feel the need to, but touching the two surfaces and connecting them in her mind suggested a different sort of understanding, more useful and intuitive.

They drove back from that visit without saying much. Violet was tired and content to doze, but the real source of their silence lay in Lawrence. The more facts he acquired the less inclined he seemed to talk. It was this dense, excluding quietness, lumpy with unshared knowledge, that had alienated Izzy. Violet felt a pang of sympathy for her. Too old and traditional to think of other women as sisters she did feel a blood tie of frustration in trying to make sense of men. What use was all this learning if it didn't make you happy? In that respect he took after his father, and a lot of good it had done *him*, poor man.

She was not brainy in that way, nor as fussed about learning things. A leaving certificate was all she could show for her schooling, but nothing more was expected in her day and full-time motherhood held enough blessings for anyone. It's true she felt inferior to the retired businesswomen and civil servants in the flats around her, 'the professionals' as Lawrence called them, always busying themselves with coffee mornings and bring-and-buy sales and visits to those less fortunate. But she only had to watch them waiting for their family to call, a cousin almost as old as them or a nephew with an eye on his inheritance, to feel she had the better of the bargain. And in any case she wasn't nearly as clueless as her son supposed. How often had he engaged half-heartedly in some discussion, assuming it did not need his full attention, only for her more down-to-earth opinions to sound more convincing?

His book was a case in point. She didn't understand it and wasn't bothered about old paintings. A copy, signed by him, had pride of place on an occasional table, a source of satisfaction and one in the eye for 'the professionals', whose calls she endured, bridling at their airs and graces. But the reasoning, the thesis as Vincent called it, went straight over her head.

'Mother,' he had said, when asked what it all meant, 'nothing worth saying about life can be stated outright. It has to be arrived at by a process of feeling or thought that gives us the impression of having discovered it for ourselves. Setting us on that path is the whole purpose of allegory and allusion. It makes for a richness of cultural reference and association which I think we've lost today.'

His eyes shone with purpose and enthusiasm, and she nodded and made encouraging noises. But this did not mean she agreed. On the contrary, she couldn't see what was wrong with plain speaking. In her view, life was built around rather simple facts and ideas which were quite capable of being talked about directly. But she did want to understand for his sake, to reward that rapt face, desperate to convince, which seemed to express the best and most vulnerable part of him.

Their third tree was his choice, a towering redwood in the grounds of a private school. It was said to be the tallest in England, although Vincent thought this a cheap and arbitrary distinction, there being, apparently, much taller ones north of the border. They were taken to the spot by the Principal's secretary, pausing to be shown the new gymnasium then standing aside for blazered boys on their way to lessons, numbers trumping age in determining right of way. The tree bore the name of the man who planted it over a hundred years before, a shipping tycoon turned amateur botanist whose last claim on posterity this was, now that his fleet of liners, once synonymous with luxury travel, had disappeared without even a sinking to be remembered by. Gabidon's Pine was a mistake, according to Lawrence, the redwood being no such thing, but rather a sequoia. Yet popular names had a habit of outlasting what was technically correct, and they both liked the idea of a native species stealing the foreigner's glory.

Violet was tired again, and he held onto her elbow as they circled the tree. He preferred supporting her like this. Perhaps linking arms reminded him of Izzy, who would have been much more stimulating company. Violet tried to make intelligent remarks about the pine, or whatever he said it was, but they fell quite flat. She kept quiet after this, but he noticed the silence and seemed to blame himself, becoming more attentive and affectionate. That was how it had been since the divorce, always trying to second-guess his moods.

A few weeks passed in which they saw less of each other. Marking, he pleaded. Research. But then he seemed to come back, as if a trial separation had failed. She made him dinner more often: ready-made food microwaved and eaten round her small table, their knees touching in moments of awkward, unacknowledged intimacy. He stayed longer, watching television and doing her chores: changing light bulbs, hanging pictures only just unpacked months after her move. She was grateful of the company, but anxious on his behalf. He should be with someone his own age, if not Izzy then another woman. Names of colleagues at work sounded promising but her attempts to find out more yielded little beyond hints at unsuitability. Her neighbours marvelled at his devotion, and 'the professionals' looked at her in a new light as the possessor of some attraction they hadn't noticed. When even freezer meals became too onerous to prepare he took over and started making real recipes, to the point where some of his cookbooks began to live in her kitchen. She caught herself thinking like one of a couple, and once called him Bill by mistake, his father's name.

Did he notice her physical decline: the new reliance on a stick, the sudden fear of falling? If so he made no mention of it. Perhaps this was how old age went, she thought, a gradual loss of movement and memory failing to register with those closest to you. At what point did one say: 'I am going to die'? Yet he seemed the dependent one, his practical help an expression of need as much as concern. He had settled too easily into a routine that was bound, by its very nature, to be short-lived, waving away her attempts to raise the subject on the pretext of sparing her feelings. But what would happen after she was gone? Could he stand another separation?

This is when she suggested their fourth tree. He was surprised, thinking she would prefer one that was closer. It was true, the prospect of a long drive was worrying. Fear of being taken ill away from home was making her more cautious. Family visits seemed too risky; holidays were out of the question. But once they set off she felt more like her old self. His new car was more comfortable, for one thing. It had been bought with the help of a loan from her that both of them knew would never be repaid.

And it was one of those lovely late summer mornings, full of the sense of things ripening. Unfortunately Lawrence's mood didn't match the weather. She knew him well enough to see it was one of his grouchier days. But in a funny way her presence was still necessary. He wouldn't tell her what was wrong but needed someone to put up with his silence. That was her contribution, it seemed. Not as good as a wife's, with the pleasures of making up to come, but more patient perhaps, and unconditional.

After the café it was only a short drive, although they got lost in some country lanes with high hedges. This time an old yew was their destination, said to have been sat under by Lambert Simnel as he reflected on the failure of his plot against the King. People seemed to sit under trees a lot in the past, Violet decided, especially when they had something important to think about. But this was Lawrence's territory and he was soon pouring cold water on the legend.

'There are no grounds to suppose that he ever came here or anywhere near it,' he explained to the windscreen, bending forward to make sure of the way.

'Why would anyone pretend he did?' asked Violet.

'Ah,' was his only reply, a sound that laid claim to the deepest secrets of the human heart, a body of knowledge too painful and complex to convey in words. Divorce had made him an expert on deception, which he seemed to believe was beyond his mother's experience or ability to understand.

The tree stood in the graveyard of a country church, which now served little more than a hamlet. The board by the gate said that the parish shared a vicar with three others nearby and that services were held only once a month. This fall from having a place in people's lives to being something they dropped in on was something Violet could relate to. For Lawrence the building was a professional challenge, and he quickly left her side to examine the stonework and carvings. Alarmed at being unsupported except for her stick, she also recognised the feeling it gave her – being taken for granted, something that hadn't happened since Bill was alive. She hadn't minded then, at least in moderation, and even now it made her feel relied on rather than overlooked. But people were less patient or forgiving these days. Take your eyes off someone like Izzy and you were asking for trouble. Worse, assuming that someone would always be there made losing them more difficult to bear.

The moment the yew appeared she knew she had been right in her choice. She edged towards it over ground made uneven by roots and the small upheavals of graves, testing the surface with her stick like a blind woman. The tree was very old and the trunk was almost entirely hollow from the ground up to the lowest branches. The wood, coppery red in colour and vertically grooved, reminded her of dried meat in the War. Inside there was crude sort of bench onto which she lowered herself, trying to do it slowly and in a controlled way but flopping the last few inches and almost falling backwards. Her back hurt. Her hips hurt. She half-groaned, half-laughed at her old bones, then made herself as comfortable as possible and waited for Lawrence.

He appeared a few moments later having completed a circuit of the church. She saw him try the door and throw up his hands in exasperation when it proved to be locked. Then he looked around and saw her in the tree.

'Hey!' he shouted, setting off in her direction. 'Look at you!'

'Could you take a photograph, please,' she said. He always carried his digital camera with him and had probably been using it on the church. She made a fuss of readying herself and tidying her hair.

He paused a few yards away and took the picture. It still surprised her, the way people held these new cameras out in front of them. The old method of looking through the lens made the whole thing seem more considered and personal.

'There,' he said, checking the image before coming to join her. It was hard to see the screen when he held it up for her to view and she rummaged in her handbag for the new reading glasses.

'Any better?' he asked, handing her the camera. How tiny it looked in his hand.

The photograph was remarkably clear – and well composed, even she could see that. All of the lower part of the tree was visible, and there she sat in pride of place as if the trunk had been hollowed out especially. Her wooden box. Wasn't this what he meant by allusion? But there was no sign of recognition, no movement or sound. Perhaps the reference was too subtle – she was new to this kind of thing, after all. She turned it sideways so that she seemed to be lying down. Surely it was obvious now. Taking the camera back, Lawrence gave her a queer little glance that could have meant anything, then looked away.

They sat side by side for a few moments, saying nothing. For once the silence was to her liking. How pretty the churchyard was, how peaceful. Old England, its time almost up, like hers. Sunshine filtered through the branches above them, warm and intermittent. Midges starred briefly in the sloping shafts of light. A bird foraged among the first few leaves to have fallen, making a dry rustling sound. Just visible to her right was a spoil heap. She could make out dead flowers from old wreaths, and the bright-green cud of newly-mown grass.

It was one of those moments when time seemed to stand still. The world had settled into position in front of her and had no need to change. Lawrence was out of sight if she looked straight ahead so that it could have been Bill, or even her father. The effect was of stopping suddenly after a lifetime's movement. Would he be all right? Had her silly stratagem worked? But even this, the last of her great concerns, seemed too troublesome to worry about now. She had done her best, that's all anyone could ask. The effect of your actions, what other people made of them – that was beyond your control.

The bird flew up into the tree. Was that a worm in its beak? After this, she supposed, nothing else would happen.

Like a Man

Jackie Gay

For Godfrey Featherstone 1939 – 2005

His father's gone and died so she's bringing the boy to mine. She's my oldest friend and we've been talking for twenty-odd years. It's always driven him crazy. 'Stop talking!' he'd say when he was little, frustrated fists and scowls blooming into full blown teenage disgust. 'Now he won't speak at all,' Sylv said, on the phone. 'Not even to the dog.' And I remember him at seven or eight, languid in a stripe of sunlight on the living room floor, arm flung over a youthful Finn as they lay together whispering, the dog's tail thumping on the floorboards.

'Can we come over?' she said. 'He's clammed up like a shell. I'm really going to lose it with him this time, Chrissy.'

'You've been saying that since he was two.'

'You'd think they were best mates the way he's acting. I doubt if he'd be so stricken if *I* died.'

'He's a teenager. Primed for a personal disaster.'

'Trust Ronnie Sullivan to give him *that*.'

Ronnie Sullivan. He was vaguely connected to people we knew, a few post-pub visits to our flat high above the city. Then one day I found him squatting outside as I hurried off to work, like a gnome, I said to Sylv later. A troll, she said. A malevolent troll sitting there under his hump-backed bridge.

He was good to me, though. I'd been ill, and he was kind. But they can do that, can't they – these drifters? Compassionate to strangers but then cold to Sylv; stone cold to the women he shared his bed with, the children he conceived.

'There's more of them,' said Sylv. 'Another sister. The mother turned up on my doorstep. I think she expected me to take her in or something. Euan didn't emerge, even for that.'

I thought of his birth. Two weeks late he was, and we couldn't help but think he was reluctant, already feeling the chill of our freezing flat, smell the lack of father beneath the clouds of Clary Sage that Sylv was burning because someone had told her it would start the baby off. The mossy, metallic tang spreading right through the block and Ronnie away already.

They arrived early this morning as a storm was mustering over the Atlantic. 'Chrissy went and moved to the last house in Ireland,' Sylv always says. It's not – Valencia is further out, and the Sky Road in Connemara – but it feels like that after the night ferry and the long drive west.

I grab Euan and snatch a kiss, he wrests himself away. His skin is burred with tiny fair hairs and I think of the times he'd sidle up to me, dawdling, chatting; long, painstaking explanations of games with names like 'Elemental Heroes'.

'Shall we go to the beach?' I say, 'looks like rain later.'

'It's good to be here,' says Sylv.

'It always rains,' says Euan.

Ah yes, but when it doesn't it's glorious – a silent exchange between me and Sylv and we're out of the house with Euan a sloping shadow behind us. 'When's the last time he stood up straight?' I whisper – laughing away our meanness, knowing the urges Sylv has to yank him straight and set him square to the world. *Take it boy, take it like a man*. But he's not a man and he's never known one, not to live with anyway, not to be close too. A couple of uncles, a few of our friends, one teacher but then he got the sack. 'Happy snapped smoking in Cannon Hill Park,' said Sylv. 'It could have been a reefer, but honestly, what planet do they think these kids are living on?

Euan charges past us, his elephantine trainers thumping on the deserted strand. 'Change the record mother,' he snaps, because he hates us discussing him over and over. Some sheep have strayed onto the sand; doleful, confused, 'like us,' I say and we can't help but laugh. We wrap ourselves in blankets and watch his silhouette, out on the rocks. He's stone still; Sylv can't keep her eyes off him. Through the silence I can hear the urgent note of my friend's wish; that somehow I can make the talking happen.

'At least he's out of that pit,' says Sylv. 'Surely this will help?'

Something's got to, I think. The air, perhaps, fresh from a thousand miles of emptiness. The sea stealing up the beach. The shafts of sunlight spiking through the clouds. God's fingers, Sylv and I called them when we first came here, camping free on the beach, singing all night round the fire. Now they reach out and anoint Euan's grubby blond locks and he's surely felt it, he's pushing back his hair and kicking off those clodhopping shoes and now his footprints will be foot-shaped like Man Friday, till the sea dissolves them along with the elephant prints and marks from sheep hooves and bird claws and the burrows of basking seals. Worm holes and fish bones and the etchings of crabs – all disappearing, into the sea, and we wait for it to happen, for the pristine beach to be released from the glimmer of the waning tide.

Euan has found a friend – the old fisherman who lives on the headland; Sylv and I exchange hopeful glances. 'Gotta do *something* while I'm here,' he grunts, 'might have known all you two would do was *talk*.' It's not – we walk, swim, cook, read, sing. I work on my veg patch and knit elaborate jumpers to sell in the summer; Sylv starts on her marking – she teaches Geography to kids who feel rurally exposed on Perry Common – and sketches. Details of this place: shells, lichen, ferns, a dried up seal fin that Finn the dog found. To Euan this is nothing and we know how archaic we seem, hype it up with exaggerated enthusiasm for each other's dabblings.

'Your caulis are looking fab, Chrissy,' says Sylv. 'They'd sell for a fortune in the right place.' It's an old joke, that our veggies and sketches and home-made clothes would transform into bags of glinting swag if not for our unerring talent for missing the boat.

'When are you going fishing?' I say. 'I tell you, I'm jealous. I bet the old man's got some stories in him.'

'He's just an old giffer,' says Euan. 'We don't *talk*.'

Does he not notice our deflation? Is he laughing inside at this ludicrous idea that time with a random man might help. We'd be ecstatic if he laughed at anything – even us, *especially* us, clowning around for his uninterested benefit – and I can see Sylv teetering, hurry Euan outside and nudge him down the path. 'Go on,' I say. 'You don't want to miss the tide.'

'So what about the funeral?' Me and Sylv are back on the dunes, watching the boat rocking out there in the distance, their heads bent together over nets and lines.

'It's not till next week,' says Sylv. 'There's an inquest – sudden death.' She's shaping sand with her hands, little mountains strung together like beads, echoing the ones which sit behind us, their tops lost to cloud.

'Are you going?' Meaning: are you taking Euan?

'Oh Chrissy I wish I didn't have to.' She swipes her hand across the sandy hills but I snatch her wrist and we both run our hands through the cool sand, building, shaping. Mountains and valleys, a maze with a driftwood centrepiece brought by Finn.

'Casanova's funeral,' I say.

'*She'll* be there,' says Sylv. The one he married at nineteen, with her two beautiful, ruthless girls, Euan's older sisters. 'Think of all his lost weekends. The on-offs, the grateful divorcees...' For Ronnie could turn his hand to all types of women, shamelessly flattering. We teased him – away with your silver tongue – kidding ourselves we'd never fall for *that*, and all the while Sylv spinning down, bewitched by his need, his blarney.

But Sylv woke up. Refused to chase after him, turn up in pubs like his other pregnant partners, demanding with their eyes and bellies. *She* would care for Euan, give up on her music, the summers busking here, the freewheeling image of herself she'd nurtured since we first heard Dylan, saw photos on the covers of his albums. We knew more by then, about Ronnie's dealing, the kids caught up in turf wars, threats at school gates which were meant for the father. Best to slide out of that world, refuse to handle stuff, hold stuff, although Ronnie always said we could make a fortune, two birds who could pass for bank clerks if we'd just bin all that hippy tat, up there in our flat looking down on the bronze mermaid sculpture, basking in her waterless pool on the roundabout on Holloway Head.

Somehow, the sun has managed to sneak under the brim of Euan's cap. He's hungry too, snatching hunks of bread while the soup pops and thickens. Sylv and I don't say 'catch anything?' or 'must have been lovely out there' and are rewarded by his presence for the evening, texting his mates and flicking over to *Killer Shark Live.* We talk of our sand-art; of diving with the seals. Dangling bait for him – a walk up Croagh Patrick, a trip to Westport or Achill. 'When are we leaving?' he barks, sharp enough to make Finn's ears prick. 'I'm going whatever *you* do.'

'If that's what you want, love,' says Sylv.'

'Why wouldn't I want to be there?'

Because he was a crook, I think. Because he never gave a thought to your feelings in his whole life. Sylv shades her face from us both. The room darkens, then brightens again, a blip in the power. I go outside and pause for a moment, gulp at the air. On the headland the lights go off in the old man's house, a sheep bleats, a bird's wing beats somewhere near. A fine mist of rain folds into my skin. I stand till I'm soaked and long afterwards, while Euan creaks around upstairs and Sylv rocks by the fire with her bottle of Bushmills.

'Some new bait,' says Sylv, the next morning. 'We'll take him to O'Mally,' and before I even flinch she's up at his door, knocking. 'Come on, Euan, we're going on a pilgrimage.'

'I'm not,' he says and Sylv says, 'You *are* Euan,' which gives him licence to sulk all the way to Sligo town. He's heard the story before, of course, how we fled the city the day the mermaid was stolen. We were staring down at her empty pool, then Sylv said, 'I'm pregnant' and we fled the city within the hour. On to the ferry then driving all night with the first curls of him in her belly and mine dead and empty then stalled by a giant hare on the slopes of Maeve's tit. O'Mally the woodman said it was an omen, that the cairn, Knocknarea, is Queen Maeve's tomb, the hare her consort and protector. We'd thought we might camp up there, that it was just a hill but O'Mally said we were right to be spooked, to heed the hare's warning.

'We could have bipped him out of the way,' says Sylv.

'It was his eyes,' I say. '*Beware*!'

We love the weirdness of this story, that we didn't just blunder through and trespass. Or perhaps it was exhaustion, the beach a better option, we pulled our sleeping bags out and dozed through the patterns of the waves. When we woke we went into town and wandered up Wine Street, stalled by the butchers' shop with figures from Sligo myths spread out across the white tiles. O'Mally told us the tale of Medb's Lump and a thousand other tales he'd sculpted into his beachcombed wood.

He's there now, scanning the street. 'Chrissy! It's been too long,' he says, although I do call in, have done over the years but it's never eased, the pang when I see the woodman. 'And this is the boy, for sure,' he says, 'the one saved by Medb's hare.'

'This is Euan,' says Sylv.

'Chrissy, mash up some tea will you.'

It hasn't changed back here, the brass kettle, the wood shavings, the single man's food: soup, oatcakes, eggs with feathers still glued to the shells. Same as it was when I'd just learned of Euan, and the woodman's nephew's serenade slipped in through the window, a song of brown-eyed girls. He'd seen us, the nephew, spied us just as Ronnie had, followed us into the shop, his arm round my waist in seconds, his merry eyes provoking.

Sylv watched me falling then and catches me now. 'Sorry Chrissy, we shouldn't have come. I wasn't thinking... I *can't* think right now.'

And I can't speak; alone with this like Euan on the rocks.

'Have you seen him?' says Sylv.

My hands trace tracks on the table, gouges from slipped chisels. 'Not for a while. I've heard he has four now. Musicians. Champions every one.'

'Oh Chrissy why do you stay?'

We thump down at the table, to chew at this, soften the gristle. 'Because of the sea, the space,' I say. Because the woodman's nephew walked me over these hills every summer, all through Euan's first five years. I prayed to fall pregnant and it worked, three times it worked but then the cramps came in waves, and I knew I'd lose him too. But my blood was leached deep in the sand by then; our beloved city harder and harder to live in. 'And the mermaid,' I say; talk of the streets for months she was, glimpsed in a garden in Shirley, flanked by Greek columns on ex-con's row. But the con had to flee and the mermaid vanished, discovered months later in an empty crack den, the sea creature from our city garden wreathed by a stale chemical whiff.

'What are you on about *now*?' says Euan. So she tells him of the stolen mermaid's fate, how we bolted to the rim; of the city for Sylv, Ireland for me. She says the things he can't bear to hear, how she knows it left him fatherless, frameless, how she longs for a different story, a better ending for us all. And all the while the woodman chips away, hammer ringing, puncturing the story, carving out new myths for Euan. Before we leave he wraps his work in paper and seals it with wax. 'For your eighteenth,' he says. 'A wee charm.'

'I have to wait?' says Euan.

'Aye,' says the woodman. 'Sometimes you do.'

Euan is not impressed with the wait for his gift. He's not impressed with the woodman, or us, or anything much. 'When are we *going*?' he says, again, and Sylv says 'soon' and Euan says 'when?'

'We always do what *you* want,' says Euan. The wipers beat, the screen and road awash.

'That's not true, Euan,' says Sylv, glancing at me for support, but I'm with Euan now, can only think in black, and red. Have to sit tight, hold on till it's passed. Finn sighs, a long exhalation.

'It *is*.'

'Euan, please. This isn't easy for me you know.'

'You wish you'd lost me don't you,' he spits.

'*What*?'

'You heard.'

'Don't *speak* to your mother like that.'

'You wish you'd lost me on some old wifey's tit.'

'We love you Euan,' I say. And although it's true and he shifts with the knowledge the words sound hollow. I drive on in silence, gripping the wheel as the storm lashes down.

They're both up before dawn, Euan cloistered in the alcove where I keep my computer.

I thread my way down to the beach and Sylv is standing in the dunes, our sculpture eaten by storm-driven waves. 'We've tried, haven't we Chrissy?' she says. 'To give his life some shape, to string it all together. But it's not enough. Not for Euan.'

'Things change, Sylv – they *need* to change. Don't beat yourself up.'

We dig our hands and bare feet down into the shifting sand. The beach is silent apart from the rattle of the old man's oars on his rowlocks and the unconscious roar of the ocean. Sylv meanders down to the old man and then steps into the boat and they're away, a trail of pock-marks from the dip of the oars. Back at the house Euan is still glued to the computer, and I resist the urge to pull the plug and drag him outside.

'What are you doing, love?' I say.

'Playing. A game.'

'Tell me about it.'

He looks up, surprised, guarded.

'I'm sorry, Euan. About Ronnie.' I say, and we're still for a while, listening to the bleeps and thuds of his battle. 'Come on,' I say, 'tell me what's what.'

'Goodies and baddies,' he says. 'Weapons, tricks, disguises. Hidden powers.'

'Just like when you were little.'

'Oh yeah,' he says. 'It's all been one big game.'

'She missed him, Euan. She loved him. But she knew he'd never change.'

'Gottcha!' says Euan. He looks at me, unblinking, his face bathed in the underwater light from the screen. 'Aunty Chrissy...' he says. He hasn't called me that in years, although he made me an honorary Aunty when he was nine and I helped him make a family tree, with photos of his cousins and dead Nan and Granddad. We had no picture of Ronnie so he chose one from the Littlewoods catalogue. 'You could have Dylan,' I said, 'your mum'd love that,' but he didn't want a flaky father, picked a man in a navy blue suit.

'Yes?' I say.

'What was dad like? When you first knew him?'

'He was good to me,' I say, not meaning to, but once it's out I know it's right. 'I'd been ill, and he was kind.'

'Ill?' says Euan. 'With what?'

'More upset than ill,' I say. Under the desk Finn starts to whine and we both reach to quiet him. 'He bought round flowers and made us both laugh. He took us dancing, whirled your mum round and round once and I'll never forget her face, like a kid at Christmas.' Like you at Christmas, I think, your excited skips, your beaming smiles.

He clicks on the screen; a ping as it dies.

'Where is she now?'

'Out at sea,' I say, and he nods gravely. Finn slips out from our fingers and scratches at the door, we follow, spy Sylv and the old man bobbing in the boat out at sea. The tide has drawn back from the beach and we can smell the mossy rocks, and something else, metallic, like blood can be.

'Finn's found something,' says Euan, and we hurry towards him. 'Finn!' I say. 'Here!' because it's a seal, flapping on the sand, and a smaller shape, blood smeared, Finn's teeth too close and we break into sprinting but I already know that she's lost her baby. I grab Finn's collar while Euan stares at the miscarried pup and strokes the mother's head. Crouching down next to her, being kind, like his father was to me the first time it happened to me.

'Is she going to die?' says Euan.

I fall to my knees, unable to stop, to stop Euan seeing this.

'The old man,' says Euan. 'He'll know what to do. She won't die. You don't die from losing babies.' So we wave our arms in great arcs till the boat scrapes on the gravel. The old man places a fatherly hand on the flank of the palpitating seal. 'Get some water,' he says to Euan, 'keep her cool till the tide comes to fetch her.' But blood is still leaking; her fins flap like wings. 'We'll have to lift her,' says the old man, so they do, over the rocks to the deeper water while Sylv and I dig a grave for the lost pup, looking up to see the seal's mermaid tail flip into the water and the boy and the man watching, waiting. We all hold our breath, the silence taut, until Euan's cry punctures it at last. 'There she is,' he yells. 'Look!' He's overcome, gladness sneaking up on him; back-slaps for the old man, kisses blown to his mum and an enigmatic smile which I remember from his boyhood, when I'd throw my hands up at his unfathomable games.

And we all watch as the seal's head follows the course of the sun's shadow out into the ocean.

Walking Wounded

Rachel Pickering

I. Sandra

No, I'll not have a biscuit, thanks. I'm watching my points at the moment and there's three in one of those. I've always been slim but the weight just fell off me after my Barry died. It was as though my body began to waste away in sympathy with his. But just recently it's been creeping back on and there's a fine line between well upholstered and middle-aged spread.

My Barry was a meat and two veg man. He never trusted foreign. When everyone was raving about that new Chinese restaurant that opened, Barry would say, 'You don't know what you're eatin'. You don't know *who* you're eatin'! Little bits of this, little bits of that... Could be your next door neighbour for all you'd know!' Honestly, he was a scream.

Dr Hitchen said it might be time to go through Barry's things to help me accept that he's gone. He explained to me after the funeral that grief is a *process*. There are stages. The trick is, according to the Doctor, to recognise your stages and sit tight till the next one.

Denial, Anger, Guilt, Depression and Acceptance. The gist of it is this: it's entirely up to you how long you spend on each one. There are some people who are nicely suited with a bit of guilt. There are those who have a taste for a bit of sackcloth and ashes. As for depression – *wallowing* is a more apt word for that. Well, it's a personal choice isn't it? You won't catch me mooning about in my dressing gown in broad daylight.

Dr Hitchen told me about widows he's met who just decide to stay with denial. They carry on regardless, cooking his favourite tea, keeping all his horse-brasses polished as though His Nibs was about to walk through the door at any moment. I can see the attraction, in a way. If you can draw this one out, you've cracked it. And if he was never very lively in the first place, you don't need to bend over backwards to deny the fact that he's not actually there. Do you follow? And, to be fair, I still often look over to Barry's chair when something funny comes on the television, thinking we'd have a laugh like we used to. But I'm not kidding myself. He's gone, all right.

The Doctor said it wasn't just the death of a spouse that could trigger the five stages. He even confided that he'd gone through denial himself when his wife left him. She packed her bag to go and he just calmly went and unpacked it and placed everything back where it was. And I went quiet and nodded, thinking, hang on a minute, who's meant to be the doo-lally one here? Him or me?

After that first appointment with the Doctor I went home and thought: I'll do the stages, fine. But I won't dwell on the boring ones. Why not skip to the more cheerful ones? Anger comes after denial and that sounded much more up my street. So anger is where I stayed, for the best part of a year.

It's only recently that we – the Doctor and I – decided I'd had a fair go at anger and since I'm not interested in depression, it was time for stage five: acceptance. Apparently, part of the healing procedure – 'the journey to acceptance' - is that I have to face up to going through Barry's box of personal possessions so here I am. And here's the box. There's not much, a few jackets, golf trophies, his favourite Wallace and Gromit mugs, some old photos and this letter. Well, I knew there would be the odd letter lurking. It's just as well I know Barry wasn't in his right mind when he wrote it.

And the photos aren't just any old photos. There are photos of Barry and I together, right alongside photos of him and his first wife, Pam on their wedding day back in the dark ages. Pam: The only woman on the planet to wear brown polyester to her own wedding. That's all it takes – one photo and acceptance gets the heave ho. I'm back to square one.

I think it was an eye opener for him when he met me, after what she'd put him through during his first marriage. They met when he was still at school and it was a shotgun wedding. His face on the photo says it all. It says: Rabbit. It says: Caught. It says: Headlights. Oh, yes, he's smiling, but his eyes aren't smiling. Pam's eyes are smiling all right though and why not? It's written all over her face. Meal Ticket. That's what she's thinking. She's five years older than me though you'd think it was ten to see her now. It's the wear and tear of bringing up those boys of hers. Theirs, I should say. Though it's hard to think they are Barry's flesh and blood. Born under a bad sign, those two. Between them they had the full range if disorders: One squint, a stammer, excess body fat and at least two 'syndromes' of one sort or another.

I don't ever tell people how old I am. But I'll whisper it if you want to know...forty-nine! I know! That's why I don't tell people. They always say I don't look it. I don't act it either. Can you really see me in a housecoat and slippers? With a manicure like this?

Barry had been married to Pam for three years when I came on the scene. He was in the Police back then and I was nursing. He'd got a leg wound chasing some yobs and I got the job of looking after him at a Police rehabilitation centre. It was a specialist centre, the idea being that it provided relief from a tremendously demanding environment for men like Barry. Do you know what? He was happier there then he was at home. He just wanted someone to talk to, someone who'd give him a kind word. They all do, the married ones. Sometimes it was like working for the RSPCA, the shocking neglect some blokes had suffered at the hands of their wives. There's more than one way you can starve a man, and it's not all about food. Pam was only interested in their two boys and they were toddlers then, so it was all about them. Nappies, feeding, howling, teething. I'm not being funny, but what she didn't realise was that Barry needed a bit of TLC too. Especially with the shifts he worked. He never actually said it but it was the classic scenario. His wife didn't understand him. I did though.

He was all for keeping it quiet. He'd say to Pam he was on a late shift so he could nip round my house when it suited. But I'm not one for secrets and I'd already said to myself: 'Sandra, this is the man you are going to marry.' I took the bull by the horns and told Pam about the affair myself because I could see Barry couldn't do it. When push comes to shove, some things are better out than in.

Things came to a head on my birthday. Barry was supposed to be on a late shift. He pulled out the stops, bought me some white gold solitaire diamond stud earrings and booked us in for a night at the Manor House Hotel. Pam rings up just as we're leaving, telling him he has to get home. The youngest was in casualty, apparently, after falling off the slide. It was only minor concussion and the boy was in safe hands. What on earth was Barry supposed to do about it after the event? The night was ruined. My mascara had run and we couldn't get the deposit back on the room booking.

So Barry dropped me back home and rushed off to the hospital. There's no sign of them. It turns out that 'casualty' was a gross exaggeration. Oh, she knew how to push Barry's buttons, no mistake. She'd got wind that he'd been with me and came round hammering on my door the following day – quite an achievement considering her son's supposed to be at death's door. I didn't invite her in. She reeked of chip fat and cigarettes.

I said, 'Can I help you?'

She said, 'Don't crack on you don't know who I am. This isn't a social visit.'

I had the chain on the door so I let her finish.

'I'll wrap that chain round your scrawny neck,' she said. 'Stay away from my husband or you'll be sorry.'

'Pam,' I said, 'let him go. Look at yourself and face facts. Is it any wonder he has had to look elsewhere? It's not hard to tackle a few extra pounds. It's like you've given up completely. Don't drag him down with you.'

Her face went from red to white as I spoke. I really think there would have been violence if I hadn't slammed the door quickly.

I do like to speak my mind. And if I didn't say it, who the hell would? I didn't need to rub her nose in it – the last thing I want to do is to hurt anyone. I'm not a monster after all. And at least the wheels had been set in motion.

The Police were marvellous. There's something so reassuring about broad shoulders. They came round soon after I phoned. They let me take my time because they could see how it had upset me. They assured me that they'd write to Pam with a warning about causing 'alarm and distress'.

Barry and I were married a year later. Barry took this photo of me on the beach on our honeymoon in Tenerife. This is going in the album. Now do you see what Pam was up against? She really didn't stand a chance. Barry said this photo reminded him of Jane Russell. He always wanted this one framed and up on the mantelpiece but I'd never agree. And have the neighbours giving me the once over every time they came round?

As the boys got older there was barely a weekend went by that she wouldn't be turning up on the doorstep with them two at her heels looking all hangdog. Or on the phone, putting demands on Barry's time. It'd be Ryan being bullied, or Lee getting into trouble with his hyperwhajamacallit. You know? When they can't sit still? He had Dyslexia too. But just because you've got dyslexia doesn't mean you can't be stupid, does it?

'In case you hadn't noticed, Barry has left,' I'd say, answering the phone to her for the umpteenth time. 'If you wanted him to be a real father to those boys you shouldn't have run your marriage into the ground.'

I know it sounds harsh but I honestly think it was for her own good. God knows it needed saying and Barry just had a blind spot when it came to them.

After our Victoria was born there was a bit of a turning point. I think it began to sink in that we were his real family now. Barry's princess. He'd spend hours with her. When I think of him now, I think of them together washing the car on Sunday morning. Chucking water at each other, acting daft.

I gave up work so I could give the best of myself to Victoria and Barry. Of course, Pam couldn't bear to see me a lady of leisure. It was all about the money with her. Always demanding cash from Barry for school trips, football strips and the rest. I'll never forget the day I was in Tesco and I saw her loading up the trolley like there was no tomorrow. I thought, 'Funny, that. Poverty stricken but she can find some spare change for Mint Viscounts at one ninety-nine a pack while we're making do with Tesco wafers.'

Excuse me. I'm going to take one of those tablets. They help with the anger. Doctor Hitchen said that whilst anger can be very empowering it could also be a destructive force...

When he was about eight, the youngest boy, Lee, would turn up at the end of the drive there every Saturday morning, dressed in full football strip. It went on for weeks. Sometimes he'd knock and ask for his Dad, sometimes he'd just hover down at the end of the front path. It was always when Barry was out at golf so I had to deal with it my way. I'd be perfectly honest and explain that no, my husband was out, he was a very busy man and did Lee mind closing the gate behind him? Once he just stood on the other side of the wall endlessly showing off some fancy football moves he'd learnt. I had to give him the hard word in the end. Told him to clear off. Golf on a Saturday was one of Barry's only pleasures in life so I didn't let on to him about this business with Lee. It would open up a can of worms, guilt-wise. And her ladyship would love that, wouldn't she? Just sit tight, I thought. Don't upset the apple cart. Sure enough, Lee did stop coming eventually and no harm done.

The McDonalds trips fizzled out after a while. Barry said himself that the three of them would often sit there tongue-tied, them staring into their happy shakes, him asking them questions about school, them doing one-word answers. They were more interested in the 'free Star Wars toy with every meal' than talking to their own father. And anyway, Victoria had her extra tuition, ballet and so on and Barry was needed for ferrying her from A to B. When she was twelve her form teacher suggested she attended the summer school for the Gifted and Talented. As parents we had a duty to ensure Victoria reached her full potential. McDonalds had to stop. The boys had started to look a bit chunky by now, anyway. Usual thing: too much TV and Playstation. And Pam was a stranger to home cooking.

In the end Pam and the boys had to move into the flat above the bakery because Barry wasn't the pushover she'd thought he would be with money. I remember it clearly that last confrontation. We happened to bump into the three of them outside Debenhams in town. We'd just got back from the cruise that Barry had booked to celebrate our Vow Renewal. We had the time of our lives. All-inclusive. Mixing with people she could only dream of: Managing Directors, Chief Executives. There was a lot of money on that ship. A *lot* of money. We were treated like a king and queen. Anyway, there she is stood in Debenhams doorway, effin and jeffin while we tried to walk away. Talk about back down to earth with a bump after the cruise.

'You've abandoned your kids!' she shrieks. 'Let *her* cut you off from your own flesh and blood!' (about *me*). Calling him a McDonald's Dad. Saying he had no time for them. That I was manipulative. Yes, you heard right. I'd handled worse than her in my nursing days, dealing with drunks and whatnot.

I said to her, 'Pam, you've burnt your bridges now. Barry won't be seeing the boys from now on. And we both know this is about the child support. You'll still be getting it if that's your worry.

But Barry and I simply won't tolerate this behaviour and he has washed his hands of all three of you.' I was very calm.

The boys heard it all and understood. They were teenagers after all, by now. I think they're too mollycoddled these days. If you shield them from the truth it just hits harder in the long run. Probably be the making of them. Barry just stormed off towards the car park, face like thunder. He hated a scene. There was waterworks and all sorts from those three. Crocodile tears.

Well, deep down Barry knew it was for the best. But she'd bullied him so much he hardly knew right from wrong any more. For a while after that last visit he wouldn't sleep at night and would shut himself in the study scribbling away till all hours writing letters to the boys. I didn't know then but he was a very poorly man and his brain wasn't functioning properly.

Barry had only months to live at that point. He found the lump in October and was buried by the following May. In a way, I'm glad we didn't know. Those last months were happy on the whole. Rotary Club. Golf. Easter in Tenerife, Disneyland for Victoria. Here's the photo of the three of us stood next to Snow White when it was Victoria's tenth birthday. After the holiday the cancer really took hold. Towards the end it was nothing but the endless letter writing. I went to find him one night and he'd fallen asleep at his desk with another half written letter to the boys. It was full of 'if you ever need anything...' and 'I'll always be your dad...'

Barry could be his own worst enemy sometimes. I didn't let on that I knew what he was writing, but I kept a very close eye on the situation. It's not as though the letters were ever sent. Most ended up in the rubbish and some were left to gather dust. I felt sick when I opened this one today. It was full of the usual stuff, the stuff I'd seen him scribbling in the study when his mind was going.

'My heart is with you. I will always regret the distance between us. Look after your mum. Be strong. Have open, generous hearts and minds and live each day as though it's a gift. I am the proudest dad in the world. Even though I can't be with you, remember that while you have my love you will walk tall and be strong, whatever life throws at you.'

It was the photos that threw me. In with the envelope with the letter were photos of *them* together when the boys were babies, on the beach, at birthday parties, at school plays. All that. I tell you, it was like a kick in the teeth. I had to keep telling myself this wasn't the *real* Barry.

I'm a Libran, which means I'm very fair and pride myself on taking a balanced approach to life's problems. Barry always said he admired my intuition about doing the right thing. What I do know is that it's not always right to let sleeping dogs lie. I remember the last time I visited Barry's grave on his birthday. There'd been fresh flowers there with a note from his 'loving sons'.

No sense opening up old wounds. The envelope is going back in the box, and the box is going to the tip. Don't get me wrong, I'm not the cold fish I'm making out. I'm going to bubble wrap two of the Wallace and Gromit mugs then post them to Ryan and Lee. I've saved the photo of Barry, Victoria and I at Disneyland and I'll send this too. It's not easy because that picture is very special to me. But, as I said, I'm not a monster. I want them to remember their Dad when he was at his happiest. The boys will get this tomorrow, all being well. They'll probably take no notice, mind – you know what teenagers are like.

Doctor Hitchen very kindly offered to drive me to the tip with the box because he didn't think I should do it alone. That'll be his car now. And I didn't have him pegged as a soft top type! Cliff and I – he keeps telling me to call him Cliff, but I keep forgetting - Cliff and I agree that grief doesn't have to be entirely negative, after all. It's possible to form friendships that are uniquely deep and supportive in the most painful circumstances.

It's remarkable really. Now I've dealt with the box I feel very peaceful. Serene, really. Dr Hitchen was right about grief being a process.

II. Victoria

It's not that I'm never going home again. It's just that I knew Mum would never let me go to London with Natasha, so I had to lie and pretend I'm on the school trip to Edale Activity Centre. It's not 'running away' and I'm not going to be a 'missing person'. If there are psychos and freaks out to get me, it's just as likely they'll get me at Edale as anywhere else. It's just like going on a school trip except much, much better. And now Creepy Cliff is hanging round Mum the whole time she seems to have taken her eye off the ball a bit and believe me, that can only be good.

So, Natasha's sister has a flat in London. Natasha says her sister has given her a key and we can go down to visit for a couple of days. We can stay longer if we feel like it. Her sister goes to the same nightclubs as Robbie and Lily Allen. She says she can get us in too if we wear heels and don't do anything stupid, like be sick. We might get tattoos while we're in London – I want a bluebird on my ankle.

I had to look like I was leaving for the wholesome Edale trip this morning and came straight to the bus station. We're going by coach to London and it takes four hours. I've had time to change out of my revolting fleece-anorak combo in the toilets but there's still an hour to wait before Natasha will be here. She didn't have to pretend to leave early and will probably be straightening her hair and putting on make-up and packing her bag. She'll probably have time to smoke a cigarette out of her bedroom window. Her Mum's really cool about smoking. She's away at a Buddhist Retreat so Natasha will be able to leave the house at ten o'clock in the morning in her jeans, no questions asked. I think the smell of her Mum's essential oils must disguise the smell of cigs.

The weird thing is I think my Mum would be quite proud if she knew the amount of planning I've had to do to pull this off. I made a big deal out of ticking off all the items on the equipment list they sent home from school: hideous cagoule, disgusting wellies, embarrassing waterproof trousers. Flask. Thick socks. Map. Nutritious snacks. And in my head I'm like: hair straighteners, Hooch top, Converse trainers, mobile phone, lipgloss. Natasha and me used a card Mum had given me for my birthday to forge her writing on the letter to school explaining that I wouldn't be able to go to Edale because we will be on a family holiday.

I know that the right thing for me to do would be to ask Mum about going away with Natasha and not lie to her but she'd say that 14 is too young to be going to London. She'd say Natasha has attitude written all over her. She'd go off on one about how when she first met Natasha she seemed so sweet and cute till the minute she opened her mouth and spoke fluent council estate. Then she'd start on about elocution lessons and how this would be an excellent idea for my long term prospects.

According to Mum, 14 is too young for anything apart from going to school, going to extra maths, going to piano, going to horse-riding, going to violin. She calls them enrichment activities and makes a big thing whenever I get a sad rosette or certificate for something, framing it and putting it on the wall and going on about how proud Dad would have been. Natasha started calling me 'Cotton Wool' because of how Mum treats me as though I'm permanently three years old.

It's hard to know whether she'd have been like this if Dad were still here. All I know is that since he died she can't let me out of her sight, unless I'm at school or at one of my classes. When Dad was here there were always other things going on, other things to think about. My step-brothers Lee and Ryan used to come round and it wasn't like we were really close or anything but at least the house was busy. They always used to turn up just as Mum was dishing out tea and she could swear they waited round the corner till they heard her call us to the table. When that happened Mum and Dad would shut the kitchen door and think nobody could hear them argue about whether the boys should eat with us.

Usually they didn't stay, but if they did, Mum would do this weird thing where her face seemed to shut down and she didn't look anyone in the eye. She'd watch their plates until they'd finished and then look at Dad. He'd push his chair back and then stretch his arms in a way that he didn't usually do and say, 'Well, boys, I didn't realise it had got so late!' He'd walk to the door and they'd follow him and he'd give them some money each just before they left. It was a note, at least a fiver – I could tell by the way he put it in their hands. Once Lee did a Chinese burn on me when Mum and Dad were out of the room. I told on him and Dad went ballistic. They stopped coming not long after.

After he died last year, Mum would keep going on about him at odd moments in the day. How he'd have liked what was in TV, or enjoyed what we were eating. I'd get this sudden missing him pain and I couldn't fit any other thoughts in my head or feelings into my heart for a few minutes while I waited for it to fade. I prefer to think about him when I'm on my own. It's like I have to get my heart prepared and then I can pick out some of the good memories from the time before he got ill and thin and stayed in bed all day. I think about us washing the car together on Saturday mornings and turn it over in my mind. I want to keep him in colour in my head, not let him fade to black and white.

It's not Mum's fault she worries. She explained to me after the funeral that she couldn't stop thinking that I'd be the next one to be 'taken' and that all she wanted to do was protect me. She owed it to Dad. I got used to her saying no every time I wanted to do things with the girls from school. Sometimes I argued, but when I did I always ended up wishing I hadn't. Mum would start crying and talking about Dad again.

Then, at the end of term, last summer, the girls were planning a trip to the cinema, then back to Ella's for pizza. Part of me wished they wouldn't invite me because I didn't want to get into explaining about Mum's over-protectiveness and how she feels like she owes it to Dad to look after me properly. But they were going to see 'Freaky Friday', and after the pizza they were going to do manicures and make-overs. So when I came home from school and asked she just gave me a look, as if to say, don't even go there.

I said I was going and she couldn't stop me. She stood in front of the door and said, 'You think you know it all don't you? Well you don't know anything. I'm stopping you and I'll show you why.' She goes into the living room and pulls this file out of the drawer and hands it to me, going '*This* is why!' I sat on the stairs and opened the file. Inside were loads and loads of newspaper cuttings about murders and awful things that had happened to girls my age. Some looked familiar – I'd seen them on the news. In some of the photos the girls wore tank tops and flared trousers that were too short. They looked like they'd been taken a long time ago. On all the photos the girls were smiling, stood next to a bike or eating an ice-cream. Some of them were school photos. I started to read what she wanted me to read, about what had been done to them by freaks and pervs and psychos. I threw it at her and ran to my room.

She followed me up and came in my room, saying, 'Take it. You can read it and read it till you finally realise why I say no and why you are not going to end up like them.'

She left it in my room and I lay on my bed not wanting to see the faces or the words ever again. I thought about Mum, with a pair of scissors, carefully cutting out and saving the bits of newspaper. I thought of her sitting at the table, punching holes in the bits of newspaper and then adding the cuttings neatly to the file and putting it back in the drawer.

For two nights I could hardly sleep thinking about the file and the girls and about Mum with the scissors. On the third night I picked up the file and started looking at it. I couldn't stop myself. I read it till it went light outside. There was a girl who had been playing on her bike and been put into the back of a van and later she was found dead. It didn't say what had happened in between the van and being found dead. There was a girl who had gone out to buy cornflakes one evening and been found months later, weighted down at the bottom of a canal. There was a girl who had been standing at the bus stop in her uniform one minute and then disappeared the next. There were two girls who had been kept prisoner in a house abroad and had been forgotten and starved to death.

After that night I realised why Mum had done it. It had worked. I didn't want to go anywhere alone for a long time after that so I didn't ask. I thought about telling my friends about the file because I didn't want them to be like one of those girls. But when I thought about how I'd say it, I just felt stupid. All I knew for sure was this: my Mum was not like other Mums. And I did not want to be like the disappeared girls. I thought about the girls for months, mainly at night, in the dark and tried to imagine what they had thought and felt and said at the end of their lives, what they had seen and heard. How long did it take to starve to death?

Then Natasha started new at our school. She'd moved up from London because her Mum had wanted to down-shift. I think it was to do with money. Natasha said it meant that her mum wasn't going to be a wage slave any more and they could spend more time together. She is one of those girls that everyone seemed to want to be around. She's got straight shiny, swingy hair and was the first girl at our school to wear Ugg boots.

Natasha started being interested in why I never go anywhere with the others so I went over all the stuff about Mum and the file and the murders. She said there was probably more chance of being hit by a meteor than attacked by a psycho. She said there was no point fighting with Mum over girly pizza nights and I may as well break the rules big time and go with her to London. I laughed but she didn't laugh with me. She meant it. She showed me a picture of her sister stood on the balcony of her flat.

Then Creepy Cliff started coming round to see Mum. They went for days out when I was at school and Mum spent a lot of time trying out different types of make-up and buying new shoes. She got her colours done, which means now she knows she suits autumnal shades like yellow and orange. And she keeps shopping for gross underwear online. It was better for a while because it took the heat off me.

Now Cliff spends most weekends round here and sits in Dad's old chair with the remote, flicking from channel to channel. I go up to my room when he's here. Sometimes he comes up and asks if I want to come and watch X Factor with them and he pretends to be interested in what I'm doing. I told Natasha about it and she said it sounds like he's trying to 'win me over'.

The girls from school get the bus into town on Saturdays and sometimes after school. They go into Superdrug and try on eyeliner, or get chips. I could never go because Mum is always there, parked up at the school gates, waving and waiting to take me straight to piano or whatever. I want to get in the car as soon as possible because I can feel my face burning.

Sometimes Mum can't get there if she's feeling under the weather and Cliff comes to school in his sports car straight from the surgery to pick me up. I know when it's a Cliff day because I can see the crowd of kids round the car before I see the car itself. They all want know how fast it goes and how much it costs and Cliff seems to arrive extra early so he can pretend not to notice the fuss it causes. When I get in the car I want him to drive off straight away but sometimes he sits and asks me questions like am I being bullied and is there anything else I want to talk to him about? He puts on a quiet voice and stares at me and leaves long gaps between the questions as though he doesn't believe my answers when I say 'No.' and 'Everything's fine.' I look straight ahead and not at his face, or his hands. He wears a gold bracelet.

I think Natasha thought I'd never dare come to London with her. Her Mum thinks it's healthy for her to learn by making her own mistakes so it's not a big deal for her. To be honest, I never really thought I'd dare go either but that all changed last week when Gran got ill. Mum came down to breakfast and announced that she was going over to stay with Gran for a few days. Saint Cliff had offered to stay at our house, pick me up from Edale after the trip, ferry me to and from school and generally carry out surveillance on me twenty-four seven. I suddenly felt like someone had put a plastic bag over my head. I needed a Plan B and fast.

So London is my Plan B. I think Natasha and me will probably end up as best friends after this trip. She tells me things that nobody else knows, like how she spent the night with Kyle Richards when she was supposed to be on a sleepover at Sophie's. She only calls me 'Cotton Wool' when Sophie and the others are around to make them laugh and I don't mind so much because I know she doesn't really mean to be nasty.

It feels strange being here at the bus station alone. People keep looking at me as though they know I'm not supposed to be here. There's a knot in my stomach. I'm going to have to get used to this. The coach leaves in 20 minutes so I hope Natasha turns up soon.

Remembrance Day

Eveline Williams

I like taking this bus; it goes all the way to Stratford. Miles. Got a pass I have so I can travel free. Freedom Pass it's called. Like to take the bus, see what's going on. Course it's all different now - since the war. Houses we had then, not all these bleeding tower blocks. You know I can go a whole day without talking to anyone that speaks English. Marvellous. Live alone I do, sheltered housing its called. Don't get much of a chance to talk to anyone. Course it was different before the war. Then there was a real community. People looked out for each other, now if you stumble or fall in the street people say you're drunk. Born and bred in the same street, knew everyone. Not there now, all gone, slum clearing they called it.

During the war I was an Air Raid Warden. Essential service - not called up. But I was fit, still am. I was a section leader. That's where I met Frank. He saved my life did Frank, and you know the funny thing? I wasn't even there when he did.

Frank. If it weren't for the war I wouldn't have had much time for him. Truth is I didn't take too kindly to him when he first joined my section. Irish. I had to show him the ropes. Scruffy sod he was. Always looked like he got dressed in the dark, let the side down I thought. Irritated me that he didn't do up the strap of his tin hat. Now me, I never left the house without a clean, ironed shirt, a fresh handkerchief in my pocket, suit sponged and pressed. That was down to my Flo. My wife, my Flo. Lovely girl she was, married her when I was 20, she was only 17 and we stayed together for 50 years. Marriage, home, kids, meant something in those days, not like today, have it off, have it away, have it out. I blame the war. One day there's the street, the houses, gardens all neat and tidy and then boom, gone just a mess, a ruddy mess. Gone. All gone. Like Frank.

Like I was saying, he was not my type. Different. Not just the accent and that, but a bit of a loner. Had all these ideas about how things were going to change, how we should overcome the oppressors, claim back the land. What did the stupid bastard think we were doing? I said to him, how come you say all that and you Irish are helping the bloody krauts. Oh he said you don't understand. Well I didn't want to understand. I wanted the bombing to stop, I wanted to wake up to a world that looked the same as when I went to bed, I wanted my Flo to stop wringing her hands, waiting every day for news of our two boys, I wanted it to be like it was before. But you could tell it was never going to be the same, how could it?

Frank got bombed out one Saturday night - direct hit - he wasn't at home thank god in fact he was with me, on duty. Well the upshot of it all was that I said he could move in with us. We had the room, now that the boys were away. So he did. You know he had a car! God knows how he managed it, what with petrol on ration and that, but he did, and he turned up at our house in it. He had nothing else. Lost the lot. Flo was impressed I can tell you. A car. Not that she wanted for anything. We owned our own house. Spotless it was. Flo, now she was in service before we got married. With a *very* good family and she knew what was what. Knew how the other half lived. She laid the table for every meal, I mean properly, linen, glasses, the lot. Spoke lovely too, brought our three kids up a treat, with manners, the right way, respectful. A credit to us they were. The language you hear kids using today would shame a squaddie.

So he moved in. I wasn't all that keen. Him being a bit of a stranger and such a messy blighter. And for someone who had nothing he seemed in a very short space of time to acquire a mass of stuff. Books, newspapers, writing stuff, clothes everywhere. But Flo sorted it. Took to cleaning the room, keeping it nice, even putting flowers in. I grew them, sweet peas, marigolds, daisies, on the allotment among the veg. I was put out at first. Why was she spending so much effort on the lodger? But when she explained that she liked keeping the boys room nice I sort of understood. She'd got a bit down, since they were evacuated. Didn't make the same effort round the house. Little things. But that all changed for the better when Frank moved in. Brought the sparkle back.

In the evening, when I got back from work, she'd have a meal ready, all set out, and she'd be smiling and nice and we'd all sit down, and Frank would tell us ridiculous stories about Ireland - made them up, the blarney, and we'd have a right laugh. If we weren't on duty me and Frank would go down the pub. I was the captain of the darts team, we were darts league champions, and we took it very serious, except Frank he never joined. He never really fitted in. It was all my mates from way back and that. As I said he was a bit of an outsider. And you had to watch if he'd had a drink - he could get very dark moods on him. Sometimes if he wasn't up to it he would stay at home. Keep Flo company. She didn't like being on her own in the house at night, especially during a raid.

Say what you like, however careless he was in his ways, he always turned up for duty. I've seen him do some very brave things. He took the job to heart. He got fired up, almost excited during a raid, couldn't wait to get stuck in. So it was a sad coincidence that he was unwell that day. He came down to breakfast and said he felt awful, was coming down with a fever, shaking. He looked flushed all right. Flo said he'd better get back to bed before it developed into something worse. Oh he said I couldn't be doing that. But she insisted - got me to back her up. Said if he went back to bed she'd bring him a hot water bottle and a nice cup of tea. So he said how could he turn down such an offer from his own Florence Nightingale.

So he missed it. The worst we'd ever seen it. They usually came over at night, made it harder for our boys to get at them, but that day they started in the morning, all day they came. It seemed as if the whole world was crumbling around us. I got a message that afternoon, in the thick of it I was, telling me my house was a gonna. They'd pulled two bodies out. Taken them to the hospital. I ran, I ran and ran and ran. My heart. My lungs. On fire. Got there. And it was ok. Flo was ok. When they'd found them Frank was on top of her, he'd shielded her from the bedroom ceiling as it caved in. He took the full force. He never regained consciousness. But my wife, my life, he'd saved her. And by saving her he saved the rest of my life.

Cold Feet

Robert Ronsson

Winner of the Button Bridge Books Short Story Prize

'German design, German engineering, Tix. They're the only ones could have done it.'

'It's incredible,' I said. 'How much water is it holding back?'

'Must be millions of gallons. The forces will be immense. It's flowing past, not hitting the barrier face on, but nevertheless ...'

John's voice trailed away. I looked out over the top rail of the barrier, which was about shoulder height. This side, the cobbles of the roadway were damp but our feet were dry. On the other, a waist-high, hoof-less stampede of mud-thick water charged blindly to the sea. It swirled and slurped as one hidden current collided with another deep in its mass. The roadway vibrated through the soles of my high heels. It wasn't only the winter evening making me shiver.

'Worth the trip, Tix?' John looked down at me, his voice pitched high. He had the same look on his face as the time he first saw me naked.

'OK, you win. I didn't believe. But this ... this is something else,' I said.

We had travelled down that afternoon. The Beemer's headlights and wipers had worked full-pelt to drag us through the curtains of rain. While we were unpacking, the clouds had cleared and now an ear-biting wind swept from the north putting its back into the helter-skelter passage downstream. We stood, buttoned up for a stroll before dinner, in the weak pool of light cast by the streetlamp outside our Tudor-beamed riverside accommodation.

John took my hand and we swung along together separated from the surge only by the confection of stanchions, plates and bolts. John sprang on his toes. He was pleased my scepticism had been as well-rooted as the trees that were being borne downstream. His hands moved in emphasis as he explained how the barrier could be erected within half a day and now gave the town's residents year-round protection.

We ducked through the pedestrian arch under the 200-year-old bridge. I wondered fleetingly whether the barrier's designers had taken into account how the ancient stonework would be subjected to new forces created by the river's containment on one side. *Of course they have*, John would say if I asked him. *They're German.*

We stopped again to look at the view across the river. The smell from the chip shop sharpened my appetite. I shivered beneath my coat and clapped my hands. The strangeness of our lower bodies being below the waterline made the damp more bone-piercing.

The bank on the other side boasted no barrier and we could see threads of reflected orange from the street-lights where the river had spilled onto the road. Cars splashed down its centre creating waves on both sides. As they turned on to the incline of the bridge, they shafted blitz-like searchlights into the sky.

'We'll just check the car's OK and then go back,' John said. He led the way through the town to the car park beyond the barrier. We made sure the encroaching water wouldn't maroon his precious Beemer and then wended our way down an alley back to the inn. Its Christmas-lit windows drew us in along shafts of red and gold.

John stood at the bar waiting to order. I sat near the fire, undoing my coat and deep-breathing the smell of wood-smoke, and thought about my answer. My best friend Ruth couldn't keep it to herself when John had asked her to help him choose a ring and I knew it would be tonight. I felt my face flush in the room's warmth – I could put it down to the open fire. John was everything I had hoped for. He was fit, bright and he made me laugh. He pressed all the right buttons. Good job in a computer consultancy – he'd never be made redundant like my dad had been. He owned the flat I'd been virtually living in for the past three months. Did I say he was fit? I knew the answer – yes; he pressed *all* the right buttons.

'Will you marry me, Tix?' John's blue eyes glistened with optimism. The restaurant was hot and thankfully most of the tables were now empty. He was so earnest. How could I not love him?

We sealed our engagement against the noise of the heaving river racing beneath the window. We slept, oblivious to the straining flood-water as it tried to break out and spend a night on the town as had been its custom for centuries.

It was still dark when I woke to the new sensation of a band round my finger. The room was hot. The duvet, which had been so comforting going to bed, now lay round my legs like a sandbag. I took a jumper and jeans into the bathroom and dressed in the light of the shaving mirror. John's tousled hair was just visible on the flowery pillow. He snuffled as I kissed him on the forehead. I picked up my coat and clicked the door shut behind me.

I pulled my belt tighter as I stepped onto the cobbles. No further panels had been added to the barrier but the water was at least a foot higher. It glinted with silver edges as eddies switched and crossed the stream but never interrupted the career southward.

I retraced our route to the bridge, but this time climbed the steps to the roadway. I was alone. The shop fronts were dark. It was too early even for the church clock to be chiming the Sunday quarters. There were signs telling motorists to turn back. The road on the other side of the bridge was now impassable.

I went to the parapet at the bridge's highest point and watched the unstoppable passage of water and flotsam as it sped into the murky distance. To my right the barrier sliced a cliff-edge of water down to the walkway. The perpendicular was unnatural, as if space had been inverted. On the far bank, where there was no barrier to contain it, the water scurried into pockets and corners seeking new sensations. It was as if it was taking a time-out before rejoining the scrambling migration.

Time stopped. A sort of hypnosis set in and my body became one with the life-form thrashing beneath the ancient arches.

'Hey! Stay there! I'll join you.'

I looked back towards the inn expecting to see John. My heart dipped. The road was empty.

'Ouch! That's freezing!'

The voice was behind me. I swivelled round. A man was paddling through the flooded roadway onto the bridge. He wore a padded ski jacket and his jeans were rolled up to the knees. It wasn't enough to escape the darkening stains as his bare feet sloshed in and out of the water. He was carrying a small knapsack in both hands at shoulder height

He emerged and rolled down his jeans. He walked gingerly towards me on bare feet. His brown eyes were bright beneath curtains of black hair that fell either side of his forehead. I guessed he was about the same age as John. He looked down at me as if we were meeting again after years apart. I'd never seen him before.

'I thought I'd be on my own this time on a Sunday morning.' He pulled open the top of the bag. 'Coffee?'

I shook my head. I looked back towards the inn. Some of the bedrooms were showing lights. Was one of them ours?

'I make it strong. There's more than enough for two.' He danced from foot to foot. 'My feet are bloody freezing. I shouldn't have done that. I only came to look at the floods. Then I saw you ... I couldn't help myself.'

'Hold on a second,' I said. I ran back to the bridge-closed sign. A workman had discarded some corrugated plastic packing. I took it back and laid it by the stranger's bare feet. They were almost as blue as the plastic. The first thing I really noticed about him was an absence. There were no sprouts of hair on his toes.

'Stand on that,' I said.

He bowed. 'Thank you, kind lady.' He straightened up and offered his hand. 'That's better. I'm Tony, by the way.'

'My name's Victoria. Everybody calls me Tix.'

He rubbed his palms together. 'Thank you, Tix. Now, coffee.'

He took out a flask with two small cups. He placed them on the parapet and poured. The steam swirled into the lightening day.

I took a cup in both hands. The heat seeped through my gloves. 'Thanks for this.' As the first taste stung my lips I remembered I had refused when he offered it.

'Bacon sandwich?'

I shook my head and watched my breath make a pattern.

'Go on. I've made too much for just me. Eyes bigger than. I decided when I saw you alone on the bridge ... somehow ... I don't know ... you must be here for me. Whatever, you could at least help me eat my breakfast.' His eyes locked on to mine and I looked away as I nodded.

There was a silence and neither of us felt the need to fill it. I had taken off a glove to pick up half of the sandwich. I bit into a mouthful of salty, unctuous bread and washed it down with the bitter heat of coffee.

'Where did you come from, Tony? I didn't see a car arrive.'

'I'm parked over there.' He pointed to a sleek sports car, Italian, parked on the edge of the flood. His abandoned shoes were pigeon-toed next to the driver's door.

'I saw you come to the top of the bridge,' he said. 'I was sitting there about to tuck in. When I saw you ... another flood freak, I thought.'

I looked down at the writhing bulk churning beneath us. 'It is amazing.'

'And to think some people come to see the barrier not the river. It's like going to the zoo to see the cages instead of the animals.'

'Yes.' I pictured John asleep in our warm bed and shivered. Tony put out a hand and withdrew it as I leaned away from him.

'She's out on this damp morning to see the river like this ... swollen, breaking out ... powerful. It's something we have in common, I thought. We're soul mates. The least I can do is share my breakfast.'

I held up the crust. 'And very appreciated it is, as well.'

'Anyway, Victoria ... Tix. Why are you here?' he said.

I swallowed the last salty gobbet. 'I came with my boyfriend. My fiancé. We were engaged last night.'

'Congratulations,' he said. His voice was flat. The breeze made his eyes water.

'Doesn't look like we're soul mates after all,' I said. 'Or your timing would be better. It looks like you're just too late.' I smiled.

He skipped only one beat. The cold made him look so serious. 'Or, just in time,' he said.

'I ought to be getting back,' I said, turning to look at the inn, hoping to see a figure in the doorway.

'Wait there,' Tony said. He was already hopping back towards the flood rolling up his jeans.

'Why?' I called after him.

I caught his response over the sound of the river. 'You'll see when I get back.'

'You're mad,' I shouted. My words carried out over the parapet and joined the flotsam plunging downstream.

I wiped my mouth with the sandwich wrapping and put my gloves back on. The last dregs of coffee were cold but I welcomed the taste like an addict.

He came back carrying a book. He had the look of an eager puppy. 'It's just ... I've nobody else to give this to. I'd like you to have it.' He thrust the book towards me.

I read its title, *Memoirs of a Shido-Joshu*. The sub-title was, *An*

English Teacher in Japan. The author's name was Tony Robertson. I looked at the picture on the back cover. The author was standing in front of me.

'It's the first copy. I got it yesterday. It's officially published next month,' he said.

'You're a writer.' I said.

'Only if it sells. I'll teach again if it doesn't, here in the UK ... or maybe Europe, I don't know. I'm sort of at a cross-roads. I'll let the fates decide.'

'I can't take this,' I said. 'Not if it's your only copy.'

'Seriously, you can. They'll be lots more. You must. Like I said, it's fate. Don't you think things are pre-determined? When a raindrop falls in the river in Shrewsbury it doesn't have any choice but to go with the flow and be spat out into the sea at Bristol. I thought it may have been like that ... when I saw you on the bridge. That's why I was so affected.'

He shrugged, showing his open palms. 'OK. It looks like I was wrong ... but there has to be some element of fate in our meeting. When a river floods, it leaves its course only fleetingly – it always has to go back.'

I laughed. 'You sound like you picked up some Japanese philosophy while you were there.' My hands trembled as I held the book. 'OK, I'll take it. But only if you think of something appropriate to write in it for me – a Japanese proverb perhaps. A dedication. Is it a deal?'

He thought for a second. He smiled and the way he looked made me think I had better head back to the inn. 'Deal,' he said. 'But you must promise not to look until you're back where you're staying.' He took out a pen and as he wrote, his face creased with concentration. 'I was thinking on my way back to the car ... what I said about going to the zoo and seeing the cages. I don't want you to think I go to zoos. I think they're cruel.'

'So do I,' I said.

'But I worked in the Safari Park once ... the one down the road.

It was my summer job when I was at college. I was on the gates to the monkey enclosure. I should have said that coming here to see this ...' He waved the pen in the direction of the river. 'Seeing this and just marvelling at the barrier, well ... it's like being more interested in the gates than the animals. Maybe that analogy works better.'

'You needn't have worried,' I said. 'I didn't think you were a zoo freak anyway.'

Tony took my gloved hand. His fingers were long like a musician's. 'Well, Tix, au revoir.' He handed me the book. 'Remember, you're not to open it until you get back to your hotel. Promise?'

'Promise.'

John was still in bed. I slipped the book into my bag and woke him.

'Where have you been?' he asked as he touched my cheek.

'For a walk,' I said. 'I stood on the bridge to watch the river. It's higher than yesterday.'

'Don't worry, Pumpkin,' he said, stroking my face with the back of his hand. 'That barrier can take it.'

We ate breakfast at the same table where John proposed. He called it our table. 'We'll come back here for all our anniversaries and always sit at this table,' he said.

'What about today?' I said. 'What shall we do today?'

'What do you want to do?'

'Did you know there's a Safari Park near here? We could see the animals.'

'If you like,' he said. 'But I think you'll find it's closed for the winter. There's the steam railway. Would you like to go on a train?'

I ignored the train suggestion. 'John,' I said. I didn't think I would have the opportunity so soon. I had to work to keep my voice even. 'That Safari Park? How do they keep the animals in the enclosures when all the cars keep moving through? I mean, some of those animals are dangerous. What stops them escaping?'

'You are a silly goose,' he said. He smiled. He reached across and put his hand on top of mine. 'You worry about the strangest things. They have a double-gate system. They work in synch so the enclosure is always secure. It's perfectly safe. Look, I'll show you ...'

He shifted the cutlery on the table top. My mind turned to the opposite bank, where the river had broken free. It was stretching its wintry toes – blue with cold and surprisingly lacking in ugly sprouts of dark hair – into places it had never been before. What was it Tony said? *When a river floods, it leaves its course only fleetingly – it always has to go back.* What did it mean for me?

I went up to pack, leaving John in the lounge catching up with the football reports in the Sunday paper. I felt in the bag for the book. I ran my palm across the front cover, turned it over and did the same to the picture on the back. Such a nice smile, I thought. I opened the book to the title page. There was no Japanese proverb. Tony's dedication was a mere two lines. It said: *If I'm in time rather than too late, you'll need this.* Underneath, he had written a telephone number.

Elemental Heroes

Gabby Bulmer

Note from the author: This extract is the first chapter of a novel written for children aged between eight and twelve. It is an adventure story called Elemental Heroes and is the first completed book in a series I have planned.

Jack Bunsen. Aged twelve.

That's exactly how they introduced him on *McTrickery's Marvels* when he won.

'First place.' The presenter slapped a rosette on Jack. 'First place, for the best entry in the *Make a Mask* section. It really is a cool super-hero mask. What inspired you Jack?'

'Um...H20 from *Elemental Heroes*,' said Jack. 'He's the best. You know the way he can do that thing? You know? The thing where he dribbles himself down to travel through rivers? I love that. Like in episode twelve of *Elemental Heroes*, the one where- '

'Of course, Jack.' The presenter eased back the microphone, swapping his tone to a chocolaty one, smooth and suited to adverts. He slipped a sideways glance at the cameras and winked. '*Elemental Heroes*, sponsors of this month's *McTrickery's Marvels* competition. The home of super-smart-science.'

Jack leaned in again. 'It took me ages to make. I used sun cream and parts of my old telly and -'

'Of course you did.' The host nudged Jack in the back, pushing him towards the camera. 'And that's great, but we need see your mask in action, Jack.'

The silent audience squashed the air out of the studio. Jack held his breath. He ran his little finger over the neatly filed eyeholes. Every minute he had spent polishing the mask had been worth it to win this. It looked good, like his silver swimming award in the trophy cabinet. Every five pence coin stuck to it glinted under the lights and he was glad he'd spent such a long time poking tin foil into the gaps and coiling bits of television wire into patterns. He glanced into the audience, searching out his mum and Gran. They caught his eye, stood and waved.

Jack drew a deep breath, closed his eyes and lifted the mask towards the lights. He knew it wouldn't really drain everything of electricity but still, he had to pretend – it was television. He waited for the special effects – he'd seen those before on this show. He listened for fireworks but they didn't come; there was only silence. The audience waited but nothing happened, nothing at all. Jack peeked at the tide of wide eyes washing over him. Had they believed him when he said his mask could drain power from anything electrical? Did they really think it would drain the studio of energy? Stupid people, thought Jack. It was only made of stuff he'd found lying around. He felt himself turning red under the hot, flickering lights.

Flickering lights?

A cry from behind the cameras made him jump. 'We've gone off air! Power's down everyone! Power – is – down!'

The studio plunged into darkness. Jack counted seven whole seconds. Someone screamed. Another person demanded their ticket money back. Jack squinted; was that someone dressed as Inferno? He blinked. Everything powered up again. Inferno had gone but the rest of the audience stood and roared. They whooped, yelled and clapped.

'Well done,' the presenter whispered, close to his ear. 'Amazing. Absolutely amazing! Look, you're a hero.'

Jack smiled. 'That was wicked,' he whispered back. 'Thank you.'

The host stared at him. 'What for?'

'Turning the lights on and off. You made it look like my mask really worked!'

The host raised Jack's arm and the audience cried out again, deafening him.

'Son,' the host yelled, shoving Jack's arm higher, 'we didn't turn anything off.'

The Wasp

Sophie Ward

Now that it was cold, the wasp had returned. That was how she thought of him, as a single being, though she knew it could not be so. A single stripy person waiting, somewhere, for the North Wind to pick up and squeeze him back into her life. She had no idea where he had been waiting, or how he found himself back by the same window day after day, every day, almost. She could only imagine the sharp coldness of the wind woke him each winter and drove him inside to her bedroom.

That he could not be the same person, not precisely, she knew, for each time she found him she was obliged to terminate his forays quite suddenly, with a book or a shoe pressed hard against his body. He was easy to catch. He flew in slow loops about her room, alighting on a wall or a shelf for some moments at a time, as though his body was a little too heavy, the effort of casting off again exhausting. She had taken to watching him for a while, the book idling by her side, letting him lift up and settle back a last few times before lunging at him with the fatal object. She thought of him, in those last moments of life, as performing for her; a miniature male Scheherazade, spinning out his final breaths with wild tales told by his body. As the weeks passed, it grew harder to kill him.

The last winter, she invested in a fly swatter. The swatter had a long handle and was certainly very efficient, but it wasn't to distance herself from the moment of impact that she bought it. She hadn't minded the clumsy literary dispatch or picking up the crumpled body between her finger and thumb, pinching at a wing or a sturdy leg and dropping it neatly into the wastepaper bin under her desk. One day she bade him farewell against her window and as she pulled her book away, she was shocked to see a copious white substance spilling from his middle. Worse, she felt it, sticky and oozing against the book.

It wasn't, she thought, so much the quality of the substance that shocked her, as its existence at all. Until then, he had always seemed so dry, her lazy wasp, desiccated. He was fat, certainly, but she considered him made of the same stuff all the way through, like a biscuit, his little shell containing more of the same crisp and air and fuzz right through his body. The next day she drove into town and bought a white plastic fly swat at the pound shop.

The first year of the wasp, she had still been married. It was in November, not long after Guy Fawkes' Night, that she went into the bedroom looking for her husband and found the wasp hovering there instead. She was stopped, staring at him, when Dennis came up the stairs minutes later.

'What's that? A hornet? Bloody hell. You gonna kill it?'

He went into the bathroom and she looked around for a suitable instrument. There were plenty of small hard objects to hand, photo frames, hairbrushes, but a book seemed to offer the most traditional and satisfactory wasp-killing experience. And so it proved. When Dennis emerged from the bathroom the wasp was gone and he had either forgotten about the insect or was not interested enough to ask about its demise. They didn't speak of it again until the next morning when the low vibrating whine of the wasp followed by intermittent muffled thuds as it threw itself against the window, woke them both up.

'I thought you killed it?'

'I did, last night.'

'You left the window open, then.'

But she hadn't. The window was closed tight; it was cold and damp outside and she didn't like to leave windows open at night anyway. She pulled at the curtain and tried to get at the window latch to let the wasp out, but it flew off as soon as she put her hand out, brushed past her arm and into the room.

'What are you doing? Helen? It's on the loose now.'

She knew he wouldn't like it, that he had a bit of a thing about most insects, but she couldn't, for that moment, move. The wasp had flown right past her, the same wasp, she felt sure, she had killed the night before and as it swept by it had collided, gently, with her bare arm. The briefest of touches but it had electrified her and she gazed at it now, bobbing slowly up and down around the room, in stunned silence.

Behind her, Dennis swore and got out of the bed, stumbling across the room towards the door.

'Want some tea?'

Alone with the intruder, she released her breath and started to look about. In the wastebasket the body of last night's victim lay intact, its legs and wings fully extended as if in exhibition. She stood on the bed and examined the window. It had a metal frame and was only single glazed, but though it rattled a little in strong winds there did not seem to be any gap big enough to allow a wasp through. From below came the muffled noises of Dennis calling her. He wouldn't come back in until the wasp was gone. She looked at it crawling over the bedside lamp and decided to run a bath. She wasn't sure why she chose the wasp over Dennis.

The third night the wasp came Dennis lost his temper. She had seen it flying about earlier in the afternoon when she was changing the sheets, but she didn't mention it to her husband until they were getting ready for bed. She made a great show of trying to catch it and in the end Dennis left and slept in the spare room. In the morning he insisted on seeing the dead wasp and then he called the council.

'It's not right. There shouldn't be wasps now. There must be a nest right here, some sort of weird mutants. Climate change, that's what it is. Bet they've come over from somewhere.'

The council told Dennis to call a private company, but nobody wanted to come out unless Dennis had seen the nest. It was too expensive, they said, to spend time looking for a nest, they charged by the part hour. Dennis said it was up to him how much he wanted to spend, but he put the phone down when they gave him a quote.

'Printing money, they are. I'll find it myself.'

He borrowed a ladder and had her hold it while he inched tentatively up the side of the house. The ladder was too short to reach the eaves and Dennis found he had no head for heights anyway.

'You go up. You don't mind that sort of thing.'

Though she wouldn't have minded the ladder, or looking for the nest, she refused to go.

'I'm allergic to wasps, Dennis, a whole nest of them could kill me.'

'You never said. How d'you know?'

'I got stung before, when I was little. My whole arm swelled up. They said I better be careful, try not to get stung again, in case, you know, it got worse.'

Dennis glowered at her suspiciously, but he gave the ladder back to the neighbour and didn't mention the nest again. That night, he fell asleep in front of the television, though it was a Friday and his usual night for going out. She sat with him until the chat shows finished but he shrugged her off when she went up to bed. He avoided the bedroom for the rest of the weekend.

On Monday, he came back from work armed with print outs from the office. They were covered with Googled information about wasps: pictures and descriptions, life cycles and habits.

'I told you it's not normal. They don't look like any of the pictures and why's there only one at a time?'

He pointed at the diagrams and waved the wads of paper around, shouted about the council and the wasps and then about wildlife in general. She didn't listen. She made a cup of tea and nodded at him when he seemed to require it but she was thinking about the bedroom and where the wasp was now.

She was telling the truth about her allergy, she had a bad reaction as a child and now she kept tablets in her handbag. But Dennis disliked discussing illness. It made him depressed, he said, everyone going on about their aches and pains. So she tended not to mention any matters medical and she found it was easier, really, to deal with all those issues on her own. After two years of marriage, she didn't feel the need to talk about her body with Dennis at all.

The wasp upstairs had arrived in the morning. She left him while she was at work, but she knew she would have to find and kill him if Dennis was going to return to the bedroom. She wouldn't care to go sleep herself, with the wasp about, probably it wasn't safe for her and yet she had no real fear of him. She had quite enjoyed his company over the weekend, letting him busy around while she read or got dressed. When she felt like it, she squashed him with her book. The choice was hers and perhaps because she knew the wasp sting was dangerous for her, or perhaps because she knew he would return the next day, she experienced no guilt about the transaction.

Dennis was still talking. He was looking down at his papers on the kitchen counter, his back turned to her and for a moment, she found herself comparing his activity with her wasp's. She rather enjoyed the idea that they were fighting over her, wasp and husband, and she allowed that her new suitor had the advantage.

That night and for the next few nights, she killed the wasp before Dennis came to bed. They slept uncomfortably, a barrier of resentment between them and when, one night the following week, she told him there was no wasp to kill, no body to view, he refused to believe her and returned to the spare room. The next morning, he came in to get his clothes and was met by a wasp hovering in the middle of the bedroom. He called his wife a bloody cow and packed a suitcase. While she was at work, he collected the rest of his things, which didn't amount to much.

Almost, she thought when she came home, almost as though he had never been there.

And that was that. How quickly he had given up. The little fight over who was to live with his wife, a minor domestic squabble between an insect and a man, had been so easily won and although she was surprised at the swift turn of events she found she wasn't sorry. The house seemed less empty now he was gone than it had been with him in it and she was free again to sit with her books and her thoughts, stare out of the window and say nothing. As for the wasp, he only came back a few times more that winter. By Christmas, he too was gone.

The following winter was the year of the fly swatter, a development of sorts. It was a mild November and the wasp didn't arrive until late in the month but one day, just as the afternoon light was fading, she heard him behind the curtain and lifted it back. He flew out and into the room as though he had never left. She couldn't say she was expecting him, but frequently and that month particularly, as she was lying in the bath or going downstairs, she wondered if he would be waiting for her when she returned. She was so glad to see him she ate her supper in the bedroom and waited until 'Newsnight' was finished before picking up her book and smashing him into the bedside table.

In December she bought the swatter and she thought his visiting pattern changed. He seemed to arrive late at night, after she was asleep and sometimes she slept through and woke to find him already up and about. One morning she found him on the bedspread itself, crawling along quite confidently but only that one time and she tried not to worry unduly as she turned out her light each night. Her wasp never tried to hurt her, never seemed angry or aggressive however many times she ended his day and recently, on the occasions when the swatter merely stunned him and she had to move in closer for another swipe, she had started to wonder why she had to kill him at all. But after the morning on the bedspread he appeared less and less and the week it snowed his visits ceased completely. She accepted that it would be almost another year before he returned.

And so it had been. Ten months and two weeks since she had last seen him and now, finally he was here. She had an idea of him that was fed throughout the summer as smaller, younger wasps fell in to her glass or fought over an apple while she sat in the garden. The day he came back, her idea was complete. Her winter wasp had shunned the world of Queens and drones, she thought, he existed outside such petty drama. His world was her world, the universe of her bedroom.

She had prepared herself for his return. Throughout October she told colleagues at work she was tired, run down. She made appointments at the doctor and came away with advice to 'rest up' and eat 'plenty of fruit and vegetables'. There was a lot of it about, apparently. She drove out to the large superstore a few exits along the motorway and stocked up on food and magazines, wine and books. The few friends who kept in touch after Dennis left were sent artistic postcards from past exhibitions in town. She wrote the same message on the back of each. She was sorry not to have seen them recently, she promised she would call soon for a catch-up; only she was so very busy at work. Maybe a Christmas drink? She had to search around for the addresses.

After her mother phoned, trying to make plans for Christmas, she unplugged the telephone. No point, she thought, in being constantly interrupted, in being harassed really, by people who had so little to do with her life. She brought a little tray up to her bedroom with a kettle and tea things carefully laid out. On the first day it was properly cold she sat in her room, quietly vigilant for the whole evening, unwilling even to turn on the television in case she missed his approach. But it was not until the following week that he arrived and by that time she was trying not to watch for him. Perhaps he enjoyed the element of surprise.

For three weeks she and the wasp returned to their old routine. She hardly left the house and only went in to work for one day where they sent her home immediately. She was amused by the sympathetic expressions on the faces of her colleagues.

He was with her most evenings and she would watch a movie or read a book. Then last thing before she turned out the light, she would reach for the swatter and swat. It all had a symmetry and purpose that felt so natural. The balance was in the sacrifice each made.

However hard she sometimes found it to end the day and however much she put it off, she was sure she was behaving correctly. But when one day he didn't return and the evening drew on with no sign of him, some of her confidence slipped. When he had still not emerged two days later she felt the first twinges of dread. Who, after all, had made the most sacrifices? Hadn't she just succumbed to her own desires, jeopardising little of any value to her? While he, who had fought off his rival and braved the elements, surrendered his life every time they met. She had been fooling herself, and now she might not have another chance to show him, her perfect lover, what she had learned.

That night he came back and she was ready. Cold had frosted over the garden and the windows were icy, but she had brought in an extra heater and the condensation ran in fat rivulets down the glass. The wasp was slow. Considerate, she thought, mindful of the occasion and of her feelings. He hovered absently about the room, over the furniture. Mostly he crawled along the curtain pole or rested beside the lamp.

She took a long bath and washed carefully, soaping her body with long tender strokes and dipping her face in her cupped hands. She cleaned her teeth and drank a cold glass of water enjoying the tiny aches in her cheek as the water and the toothpaste mixed. Lying on her bed she closed her eyes and let her thoughts drift. The wasp was beside her, how patient he had been. All this time he had been waiting, sure of her, knowing that one day, one day she would be ready. She reached out her arm and placed her fingers on the table by the light. On the other side of the pedestal the wasp shuddered and eased toward her proffered hand.

A Higher State of Consciousness

Nicola Monaghan

You walk through the door and into a wall of sound.

It's so loud it sends you off balance, makes it difficult to put one foot in front of another.

The room is immense and lofty, the size of an aircraft hangar, and it boils with people pushing and shouting and clambering over each other. The air crackles. Static moves the tiny hairs on your arms and the back of your neck; you feel it sweep your body.

The clothes people are wearing make your eyes dart about, they send you dizzy with their blues and reds and stripes and stars. The hot pool of bodies oozes sweat, which fills the air and floods your senses. Everyone's squashed against each other with their arms in the air and as you walk through, they suck you in. Your heart's pounding, you're pumped full of chemicals. You don't run and you don't fight and they build and build and it makes you light-headed. High.

People shoot past you, on a mission. They fly at you and seem to go past sooner than they get there and it's all you can do to keep yourself upright with the force of it all. The world glows radioactive; electric blue, shocking pink, the colours have a charge to them.

Then you're in the middle of it, arms stretched out to some random god. You're shouting and waving and making the room change. You pull something from the air, not solid or liquid or an object you can hold, but real nonetheless. Hard to define and gone as soon as you've touched it. It's like you're earthing a charge that flows right through you and, when you get it right, turns gold all over your fingers.

There's a lull. People move to the side of the room, they whisper to each other. The air is thick around you, the way it is on the kind of summer's day that has to break, the kind when you wait and watch for the sky to moan and scream as lightning cuts it open.

You hold your breath.

Then it's off again and it's madder than before and you didn't think that was possible but it is. It's like the floor's pulled out from underneath and you all fall through, out of control, and you've got no fucking clue where you're going to land or how hard. People scream and scratch like pigs. All round the room the lights are going mad, flashing and changing and flashing and changing and mashing up your brain with the input. It's too much to take in so it bypasses the front of your head and goes right to where it's needed. The room smells of bodies and fear and instinct. It smells of animals hunting, and being hunted.

A bell rings and it all stops. The screens and the walls are splattered red with all the numbers that have gone down, down, down, down. Like it's been sprayed with blood from a slaughter, from the hunt.

You feel blooded too, can almost smell the iron of it, feel it smeared across your face.

The floor is littered with debris. You walk, watching your feet as they crunch through abandoned trade cards. They remind you of autumn. They remind you of betting slips at the races.

Note from the author: This is a section from the beginning of my new novel Starfishing. I wanted to include this in the anthology because I have workshopped it with NAW students in the opening day of every qualifying module so far, and their feedback has been invaluable in getting this piece of work as good as it can be. I'm very pleased with the final result and how it improved through this process.

"*A Higher State of Consciousness*" was first published by Chatto and Windus as part of *Starfishing* in March 2008.

The Conversation

Ryan Davis

'Hello, madam. This isn't a sales call. It's just that we're in your area on Saturday giving free quotes and I wondered, if you would be...' 'How did you get this number?' said Carla. The voice carried on. '...interested. Your number featured on our winners list. And as I said, this Saturday one of our representatives will be in your area' 'My area?' 'So, if you want the best windows at the best price, please ring this number...' Carla put the receiver down. It was a recorded message.

Carla Breem had been sitting in her living room for the last three days. The curtains had been closed. In that time she hadn't seen or spoken to anyone. The last light to touch her face was the morning sun that had greeted her when she left the hospital. Thomas had died at 7.34am, Saturday 14th June. There was a pain in the lower part of his back, then he started to pass blood. It must be some kind of infection, was the thinking. They gave him a scan and a dark spot was found on his liver. The consultant told him that he could have chemo, and if he responded to it, things could be good and work out. Cancer bloomed black and quick like an oil spill. He was thirty six.

Carla went with him to each session. Held his hand tightly as they walked to the theatre. 'I'll be waiting for you, when you're done' she'd say sternly and gave him a smile, then when the door slid shut, wept. It seemed such a mystery. What lay behind those doors? Carla saw the chemo as a type of large ray gun which gathered together all of Tom's energy and shot it back at him, in to the centre of the tumour. She could never have imagined him to be so weak. He was 6ft 2in. He built cars. When they met outside Murphy's ten years ago, she asked Tom for a cuddle. She said it was because she felt cold. He put his thick arms around her back and his head arched over hers. It was warm, safe and at the same time it turned her on. After the treatment he would have to hold on to Carla to get from the car to their front door. Auntie Janice was the last person she spoke to and saw. She drove Carla back home in silence on that morning. Just before getting out the car Janice gripped Carla's hand and placed in it a small brown bottle of pills, 'Have some of these, when it bites. Darlin' believe me, they really take the edge off.'

Carla looked at the thing in her hand, then up at Janice. She kissed her Aunt's cheek, got out the car and walked to the front door. Janice shouted to her, 'I know you've always been a quiet little thing, but give us a call if you need to talk'

The first day was spent crying. She remembered their honeymoon in Spain. The day trip to Gibraltar where the monkey ran off with the camera. When she cut her finger chopping chilli, the first time she cooked for him. He raised it to his mouth and said he would suck out the poison. The time he took her to the butterfly house at Blenheim Palace and told her not to tell 'the boys' about how much he enjoyed it. She remembered how ambitious Tom was. He was on the manufacturing line, it wouldn't be long till he was a manager. But then they started to lay men off. It was called scaling down. His job was safe, they assured him. Six months later the company was sold to a Japanese firm and manufacture relocated to Malaysia.

How can a person imagine how another person will turn out? Curled up on the floor, a loop of every time he hurt her, every disappointment and every embarrassment he brought into her life circled the room. The same strength she loved became the thing that made Carla hide in the bathroom. The sound of his fists on the door rattled around her head. If it wasn't for her holding him back, it would have never happened. She stopped talking after that. Only if she was asked a question. The days she spent where she thought only of him (because she was afraid that if she didn't, he would know) seemed such a waste. And these were the thoughts that she could remember the most? She took the tablets. Slept. Woke. Went to the toilet. Slept.

On the second day the room had become her world. The tablets swilled around her sweaty body. She saw him, sat in his chair and tried to talk to him. His voice sounded different. Calm, assured. She tried to rile him, tease him. Make him take the bait. She screamed with frustration. She threw cups at the chair. They seemed to miss him every time. All he would say was,'Yes'. 'Yes,' in a soft, feminine voice, to questions or accusations. It went on through the night and the more she shouted the more tired she felt. What was she doing? She was screaming at her dead husband. He didn't get angry. He didn't raise his voice. And he could only give her the same answer. The frustration turned to guilt. Carla knelt beside the chair. She tried to stroke Tom's head like she did in the hospital. Only now, his hair was back. Before, it was bony, and dry. Now his head was soft, velvety. She apologised to him for throwing the cups. For screaming. For not talking things through. Carla dropped her head and began to whisper. Did he like it when she stroked his hair? 'Yes' Would he forgive her? 'Yes' Did he love her?

'Yes'

Carla sat on the chair with him and the questioning went on into the night. When she woke in the morning Tom had gone. Sunlight rumbled behind the curtains. She wanted a cup of tea. She wanted to see Auntie Janice. The phone rang. It had been ringing since Sunday but she couldn't answer it. Carla decided to pick it up. 'Hello, madam. This isn't a sales call. It's just that we're in your area on Saturday, giving free quotes and I wondered if you would be...'

The Free Word Competition

To launch the new academic year in 2007 we ran a competition within Birmingham City University to write a story of any style and on any subject using just 60 words plus a 'free' word, which was also the prize: lunch. The full set of entries will be published elsewhere: for now, to whet your appetite, here are the three winners and two runners-up.

Nick Le Mesurier

Winners

1st Prize

Meat
Sophie Ward

Sally saw a special offer on Luncheon Meat in the book of coupons. What was Luncheon Meat? Was it like Spam? She'd had Spam before, at her Aunt's house in Wilmington when she was six. It was all right. She wouldn't mind it again. And it kept. That was why they'd used it in the war, wasn't it? She clipped out the coupon.

2nd Prize

Family Photograph after Lunch, Osler Street, Ladywood, Christmas 1920
Derek Littlewood

That autumn I worked through Elizabeth David's *French Provincial Cooking*. Mother sipped reflectively: 'A well-flavoured broth, we had rabbits at home, nunk-nunks we called them.' She pushed the dish away. Years later, I saw the photograph. Mother, aged twelve with her sister, Annie. Annie wears a stole, while Edith has her hands inside a muff. Silver fox angora, the height of fashion.

3rd Prize

Love and Regret
Rachel Pickering

My new guinea pig nuzzled my hand. Sharon watched from the garden gate. 'His name's Freddy,' I said, gleaming. 'His heartbeat tickles my palm!' 'Can I hold him?' asked Sharon, reaching over. 'No.' We grappled, small hands on black fur. 'Stop!', bellowed Mum, but by then it was too late. Freddy was limp.

After lunch we dug a tiny grave.

Runners Up

Lonely Lunch
Liz Nichols

She lowered the menu just an inch.

She shouldn't have followed him.

He looked like an advert for a high performance razor, but he had his clothes on. She imagined him without.

It had been such a long time.

'Are you ready to order, Madam?'

Over her shield she noted the usual gasp as the waitress saw her damaged face.

Tolly's Little Problem
Robert Ronsson

'Lunch!' Tolly's face contorted, his neck snapped. 'Lunch! Lunch!'

My husband, Tolly's stepfather, stormed in. 'What the lunch! Have you seen my lunching glasses?'

I gave him the stare and Tolly spat and flicked his dinnery fingers. I sighed. Soon the subterfuge would be pointless. We were in the countdown to Tolly's first day at school.

How long before he heard the word, 'Fuck'?

Poetry

Green Ribbon Song Cycle

Rena Brannan

Cotton Nero Axe ii
(Januarie 1st 1402)

Note from author: The Thorn character Þ and the Yogh character Ȝ are used in writing Middle English. Thorn should be read as 'TH' (thanks) and Yogh should be read as either 'Y' (your) or the 'GH' (laugh or high).

Ȝoure lyf heiȝ hanged
Ȝoure wilyng nat lufs
WiÞout gilt lurks to frese
Owneself
And alle yow maad
Graunt knyȝte Þe trouÞe hires tak kynde Noot to hire and Ȝoure hertes And Ȝoure yifes Fader systir to yow Ȝoure lust Þe dremes of siÞe

Þe werd Oedipus of Ȝoure midde nyȝt
Lessid in taking Ȝoure manhood
Liche crist cyrcumcydyt

Whoso yow nice promis wonte kep
Gnomen after alle doon
Gnomen,
Tulk alle before Þe ryche kine court
Boren folie to blod Ȝoure
Mokke and schame yow Þe broÞerhede wyl
With lees laȝyng eyen and torne lymppede kne

Glouten

Reuelry, bryȜt grene gordel
Hor a dyerfulle schrewe yow war daffed aboute Giffyn deer, boor, and col-fox Ȝiftes Þen More Þen yow neded Þe fyrst dame rampe
Hore Ȝoure chyvalrie cude Harlotrie doon

Kithyng yow to kulle hir Baldric
Flooke Þe Twies To-ward ape doubbel
But Þe derling willen wurse to gliffen
A Raganelle
And yow willen to-cleef in luef
And sche willen Þe lel wlite
Þet yow al-day wantede
Bothe wele ugsom and ryȜt praty
with gnarred toothe and scorkelyn swouȜ swarde Sche willen swekten soone yow efter berȜen hir And Ouir mykel tried for a wyf to wone Taken in a-gȜein by ryche kine Arthur Alle Ȝoure bayn dæde hafd strengen

Þe raunson of Felix Brutus
Whoso yvel preef honoured yow do ber

A noot soote bitoȜen drounen
peere eppel sed scarlet reed and mirye
Hym cyano poyson
A wodwo cume
Awaywarde knyȜt
A fayrehede burde

Þenne straunge wappynge Ȝond Þe rowans
Under Þe chapele mone
Hir draf yow bald lunatik
To Þe hende of Ȝoure. hares frakly drawen Þet Þyef Morgane le Fay Yow luef hir ryȜt trewely Yow dide trewely

Cotton Nero A.x.e ii Translation
Anonymous II (February 11th, 2009)

You've been strung up
Marked and Worthless
Lost your good looks
Your cool ladies touch
Longing after your old Uncle's sister
Every body knows it Master Sergeant
She's your Mardi gras

Better poke out your eyes
On the coldest day of the year

Snowdrop

You've said it twice before
but talk comes filthy
Cos you're human
Divine
Your Green Platoon will tease you to ashes
But death is not for you

Hardheaded fool
It's a Roman Holiday for the desert troops
Celebrate Green Beret
Confess your sins
How a woman had you
Circled your little rounds
Gave you steak, ham and chinchilla fur
Intoxicated
She took advantage
Kinda like an Uma Thurman
She told you to kill William of Orange

And you did
You've got to admire the chick

And the next time you fall in love
Ugly is all you'll get
But you will fall in to love
Like a red rose wood
Ordered from the round table
The girl you've always wanted
With a hot and cold
Overbite
When she dies
In that tower twain
As Your love forever dies
You'll know

Arthur's fucked you again

Now you've got suicide bombers on your tail
The only friends are the ones that never left you
A fairy princess and a corporal named Felix
Don't know what they saw in you
Red Meal ticket I guess
Through the trees and under the full half moon
Your hair standing on ends

Claim your badge of dishonour
You've lain with the brunette Enemy
Really truly you did

Cotton Nero A.x.e ii Translation
Anonymous I (February 14, 1965)

Your life hangs high
Your love unwilling
Innocence lurks to terrify
You alone
And all you meet
Grand knight the truth they take not kindly
to theirs and your heart
And gives your Aunt to you
The dreams of your desires

The Oedipus of your mid-night.

One foolish promise you cannot keep.
Human after all
Man
folly born to your blood
The brotherhood will mock and shame you
With laughing eyes and weakened knees.

Gloating
Revelry, a girdle of green

How you were duped by a fatal shrew
Given deer, boar and fox
More than you needed
The first femme fatale
Caressing your chivalric code
Telling you to kill her Baldric
Finally to collect your double indemnity
But the one next will be worse to look at
a rag-a-muffin

You will fall in love
And she will be the true beauty
That you've always wanted
both ugly and pretty
With snarled teeth and scorched skin
She will die soon after you've saved her
Too much choice for a woman to want
Taken in again by noble Arthur
All your good deeds have strings

The ransom of Felix Brutus
Whose honourable curse you do carry
A bitter bite drowned apple seed red and merry
A winter's cyanide
A wodwo
A Knight
A maiden

Then barking through the rowans
Under the chapel moon
She drove you lunatic
To the end of your keenly drawn hairs
That Morgan le fey
You really loved her
You really did

Shura: March 3, 1965

Consultation

with my father his lock of hair fisted in my hand as I grabbed him playing at the morning table.
Breakfast, I am born

She picks me up in her arms
My hair a wig of contradictions

She puts me on the mattress
I was born on
She made love on
She and I will die on

Rena: March 17, 1965

Consultation

with my mother her black and red abacus in my head as I count rice and soybeans
Lunchtime nap, I am born

I hold onto her arm my swollen fingers fist and twitch
A signal
An alarm if she moves
But my alarm doesn't work

I played concert piano
At four
And wrote poetry at six
And wedded at twenty-seven

That me never lived
When I wake she is gone.

Shura: March 25, 1969

She did this once your other one
And now mine will do it again
And she will do it better
And take me this time

She holds me
As the perfume swirls around us
Wild Strawberries
The odour hurls across the stench of the closed
Windows

She takes the last few breaths from
Me.
And whispers
Baby
Sulphur sweet ignites her lungs.

Then we curdle to sleep

Rena: March 30, 1975

I've been looking for shura all of my life
I pass you on the street
once every ten years

I see Eddie
You've been looking too

Funeral Chamber
(April 6h)

The spring underneath drowned
The Rowan Tree on the first of April
And the Lepidoptera called Mike.

I wished the builder drowned under too
But no such luck for that blessed fool
All I have is the warped tobacco floor
and a discontinued Egyptian toilet
Called Headriss with a broken guillotine
Nearly beheaded Angela the day she came to dine
Brain tumour just benign

I won't die at home
I think I'd rather pass at the old chapel
I'll lie on the six-foot tombstone
In the swarming dew
Alongside the bluebells and leylandii
AI, AI
This makes sense for a man like me
Walks in a circle of concrete
Little terrier called Tracy
She'll need a Zima frame before I do.
It's a shame about the vicar
working at the
Petrol Zoo

Worse I won't die
Because the Rowan drowned
And then I cut it down
Stumped to nothing

I wish Arthur told me
But he never stopped on his way
Hurrying for his two nil game
He didn't know Mike choked
In a cancer solution
Butterfly wings radioactive

I sat with Mike on the Great Western
Took him all the way to Kemble Station

But the bad luck came after
The Rowan Tree fell
Mike died and my home went to Hell
Lost everything even the bells

I grew up on a country road
Never went back

Now the M4

Ensorcelled
The Story of Lady Bertalak and the Fugitive Gawain.
(May 5th)

You and I have killed a lot of things.
That squirrel was the last thing when you were 10
and I was past the first blush, a rose pricked

It was the shotgun he gave you the old man
What was it that he wanted rid of?
His wilted face.
His damp body
His oozing feet
Chasing after pastures he construed.

We weren't killers
But we put on hats that said we were
And a breastplate made of oil and myrrh
And that stupid cat followed us for days
Until we loved it, feed it, and killed it

We never did anything for fun
Except
Scatter poppies and shoot that shotgun
And murder Jack-o-Green
To quiver the inside of your belly
The womb of my womb

I often wish for that skillful belly of yours
If I were a Man you respected
We would have ran better
Running away to another hundred yards
One hundred years later
Another squirrel

Maybe even a 14 pointer
A boar's head inside the firehouse
With a flame retardant pink dress and a bow
But Instead I'm a doe
Slit open
And a better sacrifice
My face stretched around my skull
My body hung out
My feet hunched around a rope

We should have killed the old man
We should have killed him a time long ago

Amuse Gueule
(June 22nd)

Savour the bullet
A gem inside my mouth
Scrapings rubbed between sticky forefingers
Licked,
Dull.

Strawberries and Cream near Worple Road

If I prove how much I love you with each kiss
Will you forget this green Minotaur's promise?

You are the candy of kings
I am the curse of queens

The only passion
you will ever know

Lord to these damned things
I will bend my knee

And rummage over your summer heat
In a home of winter ash
Cut the kids hair and brush their teeth
Walk the dog under the crooked wheat
And what will you do?
Leave your boots inside our bed
And use me
Proper

I wonder as I work on the telephone lines
How far up the pole can I climb?

Swallow this small pomegranate seed
Add your sorrow and Turner's mead
And it will grow to your disgust
Pregnant and never birthed
Without honour or holy right
Then you will be mine

A morsel, a crumb, a tender bite.

Junk Pile
(July 13th)

That evening outside the A and E
Head bashed against some asbo
Lady Godiva
Scavenging for a load
Needle busted vessels
Digging for gold

The head is a hard sale
Especially this far into July
Used heads don't sell
Rotten summer meat

And when your Gods tells you to sit up straight
And pull up your socks
Even though you have just one limp eye
And a tire iron for a leg
And the bombs keep spitting tongues of silver nitrate
Nitrate of silver ammonium and sulphur oxide
Good clean stuff for mamma's hair dye
I'll tell you then the story of your skull

Bashful

How it was stitched together by Frankenstein's Eye
Blood gouged sinew torpedo machete fat hanging from broken oily lips
fattened with foi gras
fattened with gold arches
Killing is easy in the English summertime

As it always was when you only had a head.
A head the size of a silver dollar pancake.

So you thought you took
My heart on that bed
Kissed me once kissed me twice
Then you realized
you took my sun
instead

Quietus
(August 17th)

We owed King John and the August Plague
Just another flower vying for earth
But eventually they took each of us

I had a chair
With three feet
That I carried
With my mother and my father
Like an imbecile does
Who knows that all bets
Are just Opal Fruits
Chewed and forgotten
And then regurgitated
Wrappers spoiling the lousy
Floor
Caster
That's what they called us
Caster or
Slants

We never afforded dance class
We never afforded music
Or anything more than we ever afforded

Asked to forfeit our debt
Dice cards and stone
Welshered our neighbours
Our friends and finally
Our families

We were asked to give for
something we didn't own

And when they laid me next to my beloved
They had all and I with only the bone of her hand
But even she had forgotten how much love went into
dying

Zeitgeber (Zite Gayberr)
(September 8th)

In a year
I'll live a fortnight
More than you.

I'll betray all of you
In a way that will leave
Your boggled corpses
Arid and fettered
Amongst the island
All of you will lie
The Fisherman
The Surfer
The Breadmaker

And the Dealbreakers
All of you will host
My dreary brood
I will find you where you have laid
Living squalor
With one or two maids
And you will dust all
The heathen snort from your
Cracked and shingled lips

This is my land now
You will not have one inch
I will live on it
From sunrise to set
I will bolster the stars at night
I will be the keeper of the light

And rising from the
Mourning tide halved
Suckled and succour
I'll live a fortnight
More than you

In Reverse
(October 28th)

It was you I hit on the 31st of October 1983.
My headlamps bumped over your feet.
The woodpecker billed it's nose
into the only other witness
A creosote telephone pole.
Oiled Conkers slapped the bonnet
Clunk
Clunk
I took my dad's advice and hit you straight on.
He always said that it was better to save yourself than to risk a broken neck.
I often wished for that broken neck.
Instead you've been swallowed up
Buried deep and now a Spring comes
And often an owl
Towit
Towoo
They've mislaid you

Circling the moonless highway
Motoring the mindful step of your shoes.
I wonder as your breath delays my morning sleep.
You are every relationship I've ever had.
You are the corner of my deceit.

The Price of Crude
(November 7th)

You taught me something I never should know
My brother Yes my brother
Big Wheels and candy cigarettes
On a flat road in a flat town pierced by a green thumb
Taxing down a runway a strip of fast food joints
And fast food cars

Tar Barrel Flames
Chuppa Chops
And mothers who cry on Mother's Day

Dressed in maroon waffle ties
And pressed cotton shirts with jersey letters on our coats

We never dined with the Homecoming Queen.
On the fifth of November
We had no reason
We passed her in the Great Hall
Bowed to her every need
And won every game
From Plymouth to Athens

We made it up as if we always knew.

How to treat girls without a harsh word
How to pry apart lips within the alphabet
And place each kiss one noun one verb
Until marriage the only promise to ask for

And we obeyed
As men do.
Lost among the ruins

But let's talk about girls
Girl's gifts
Girl's glands
Girl's gams

We made it up as if we always knew

How to treat men with thumping palms
How to love with silent shrugs
How to sit side-by-side
Nothing much said until death parted us

We obeyed
As men do

Lost among the ruins

But let's talk about boys
Boys with brains
Boys with brawn
Boys with bombs

You taught me something I never should know
My brother Yes my brother
Big Wheels and Candy Cigarettes
How to blow
Smoke rings from my glands

And now you will never know
My flat palm in a girl's hand
My caked calves in a boy's grip

Good brother
Amongst the ruins
I miss you

Ted and the Pearl Poet
(December 30th)

Sometimes I walk the York Moors
Usually on the shortest December morn
Full stone circle I have arrived
It's hard to give up the junk beat
Preening
My words all over the resurfaced weeds
Potholes sinkered on sunken slip roads
I pick up the dead along the way.
I heard you lost yours
These things happen
Not your fault.
Not yours at all

On Parts of these lanes
Suicide outnumber murders
We peddled this place
Together
and drank the earth's blood
The brewing beer
It smells of an old man's urinal
Iron and lavender
Old Peculiar then
And Old Peculiar now

It often makes me feel sick
That I'm standing on the same jot
As you
It sours the milk in my tea
And corrodes the enamel on my pegs
But I've learnt to glug down through my nostrils
Sore as that might be

You and I have built islands
Castles with moats
We don't know how to leave
Two Rapunzels up a tree
And we don't know how to swim
But we learned when we were kids

A moat can drown you
Because a moat can drown your child
Of course you and I learned how to swim
When we were kids
But we stopped knowing now

I lost my Pearl and you lost yours
I dreamt of yours on Fitzroy Road
Walking down Primrose Hill
Passing through Regent's Park she scuttled into a boat and
We skimmed the Lake towards the Tower
She made me give up my boots
I took them off and placed them in the water
She asked for my feet
I took them off
And she laughed at how ridiculous I looked
Holding my toes
Mister you have a blister

I saw the pus bubble to the surface
It's my little girl I said
Will you take me to her?
I'm going the other way
If you want to find her
Ask Edward he knows where all the little girls go

With the twirling derling wodwo

Todtnauberg

by Paul Celan

Translated from the original German by Anthony Mellors

'Mr. Evans sat starkly upright on their log'

Wolfsbane, Eyebright, the
homeopath let spoil
half the spec trade
talked into blindness,

(acid-tolerant),

water drunk
from the well with the
star cut above the spout,

in the
hut

in the
logbook

(whose name before mine?)

inscribed there
something about hope, today,
for a thinker's
word
on the way
in the heart,

woodland clearing, skewed,
orchis and *orchis*, paired root apart,

limited hangout, wolverine,
a green light

the driver
witnessing
(lately sore eyes),

bludgeoned
log-strewn paths
(now a 'circular walk',
the hut verboten)
bogged,

sodden,
mulch?

Subnarcosis

by Andrea Zanzotto

Translated from the original Italian by Anthony Mellors

Birds
harsh boundless twittering
on a winter tree
something harsh
perhaps untrue only
born too soon
struggling to speak
but certainly for we who listen
- alarmed
distant
- subdued too
far off
birds: an entire city
swarming closed
glottal joy
insights and lime-spattered canons
a closed so-so-significance
not even *in-fans* but
adult occult in its zero-degree

(dispersed species of sleep
that will never return to me).

Life Writing

You Are Who You Know

Bruce Johns

Malcolm Benefer is dead.

Don't worry if the name means nothing to you. I'd forgotten him myself except for occasional reminders, walk-on parts in more vivid memories. But his face jumped out at me from this morning's paper, the shock like that of seeing an old friend somewhere unexpected, blank familiarity followed by a turnstile click of recognition and surprise. The photograph helped. Set in a tribute almost a page in width but only two or three inches high, a caricature in print of his gnome-like stature, it seemed to date from the period when we were neighbours. He was gazing steadfastly away from the camera, as if aware of its attentions but not pandering to the shallowness of the medium. After such a long time this standing on principle in a matter so small struck me as typical. So did the vanity in the pose, itself mocked by a crinkle of humour around the mouth and eyes.

The obituary, on the other hand, made him seem a strange, almost exotic figure. The early years as a farm worker were new to me, of course, as was the almost heroic self-education. But why didn't I know about the International Brigade, the paragraph in the 1945 manifesto? And was he really such a heart-throb of the London Left before the War? I tried to imagine him as a young man newly arrived from the country, his shortness and pluck a cause for women comrades to espouse, perhaps, something closer and more amenable to their sympathy than Abyssinia or Spain. It makes me wonder how well I really knew him. Even today it still feels like friendship, however lop-sided and temporary, but maybe I was only an acquaintance after all, useful on occasion but never close to the man.

How strange, then, that after all these years I can give you the exact date of the one whole day we spent together.

You'll need some background if this is going to make any sense to you. A bit of time and place. We are talking about the 1970s, before the advent of almost everything people think of as modern. Take the city itself, where all of this happened. Full of churches is how I remember it, crooked chapels cheek-by-jowl with pretty pubs or outfitters selling tweeds and the trappings of country sports: shooting sticks, hip flasks, fishing rods. Everything half-timbered or old brick except for concrete and glass where the bombs had fallen. In those days nothing was taller than the cathedral spire, visible everywhere but curiously hard to get at, an eccentricity to baffle tourists. And then there was the Art College, wasted down a side street, where I once got work as a life model but didn't have the nerve. The surrounding countryside was visible from most places – still my definition of the right size for a city, though much harder to find. And everywhere that same accent, ripe and slow-witted.

This was where I grew up, and still have some of my houses. But property was theft in those days and I counted myself a rebel. Long hair, girls wouldn't look at you otherwise. A certainty that music could change the world – the lyrics laughable, I see that now and if I didn't my own children would remind me. Clothes bought from charity shops: collarless shirts, jackets that old men had probably croaked in, pullovers made fashionable by being three sizes too large. It was a hand-to-mouth kind of existence: odd jobs when I could get them, with the fall-back of the dole – something I keep quiet about now. My school friends had gone to university but I flunked my exams so I made a virtue out of being a free spirit, learning from life. Humping bricks, cash-in-hand. Haunting pubs, on both sides of the bar. Hunting market stalls for bargains. What was I reading then? Lord of the Rings and Siddhartha – the set texts of bedsit hippies. I knew a drug dealer who called himself Gandalf and measured deals on a set of portable scales that were almost certainly rigged. He is still the most out-and-out capitalist I have ever met, and believe me I've known a few.

The memories of that time are random but evocative and almost all of night. The dark-room pallor of red light bulbs. Patchouli oil, sickly and decadent. The tip of a joint glowing and fading as it passed among us.

I kept moving, another article of faith but in reality driven by restlessness and rent arrears. Shared flats when I was lucky. Shabby sub-lets in student dives. Once an ancient caravan with plastic taped over the windows, cheap but I nearly froze. How I ended up in the house on Milton Street is lost to me now. It was a cut above my usual address with its stout furniture and air of better times only just departed. The other residents didn't fit the bill, either. A young man not much older than myself who worked in a bank or an insurance company, his cheap suit and plastic lunch boxes standing for everything I was trying to avoid. A middle-aged nurse who occupied the top floor and took a motherly shine to me – or a professional interest, or even a romantic one: I was never quite sure. A Syrian postgraduate and his English girlfriend, whose cats, spoiled like children, preened and arched and capered all over the house. And Malcolm, his rooms opposite mine across the wide, ill-lit hallway, with its gallows of a hat-stand and death-trap switches hanging from the wall.

We met soon after I moved in, and quickly went from neighbourly greetings to gossip about goings-on in the house to conversations of a more interesting kind (the iniquities of a recent law, beer, the female mind and how to fathom it). Perhaps he was using me as fieldwork, probing the beliefs of a generation in revolt against his own, attracted by their dissent but sceptical about the calibre of thinking – and curious, like most men of his age, about our claims to sexual freedom. Everyone was taller than him, but he had developed a way of dealing with this that involved standing at an angle to the other person, making the absence of eye contact seem enviable, his own line of sight fixed on a more interesting or informed point of view. I see him wearing a mustard-coloured corduroy jacket and a green waistcoat that had wooden buttons with pale crosses in them like buns. Or was that someone else? After so long it's hard to tell. His face I can be sure about, having the photograph beside me. Pale it was, from years spent in libraries I suppose, with a sharp beak, the lips thin and dry as if displeased, the eyes quirky, darting, small.

His hair, with its firebreak of a side parting, was sealed by a layer of grease that smelled fatty and sour. Not much going for him, looks-wise, but stoutness lent a certain gravitas and tiny feet an expectation of nimbleness - in movement and, by extension, thought.

He had a wife, Marigold, but you rarely saw them together. The extent of his dependence on her, when I discovered it, was comic yet touching in a way. Ample and down-to-earth, she was by no means simple but of necessity a simplifier. Confronted with a blocked drain, he would have pondered the history of domestic sanitation while she straightened a coat hanger and rolled up her sleeve. You get a division of labour in most marriages and it's not always clear who is to blame, although in this case my money's on Malcolm.

The image I have of Marigold, filtered now through years of forgetting, is of activity fuelled by impatience, ostensibly with the world at large but originating with him and then turned outwards to deflect it away from the more important centres of feeling: loyalty, affection. She was a teacher, presumably reliant, given their lifestyle, on supply work that denied her the satisfactions of a career. But I reckon she still earned more than he did, with his grants and honoraria and conference fees and fellowships. There would have been royalty cheques, too, of course, but they must have been paltry. How many people read, let alone bought, *The Shaken Tree: Rural Protest in Three Counties* or *Rise and Shine: Morning and Work in English Culture*? I certainly didn't: these titles come from his obituary. That's also where I heard about the collection he edited of essays by Dietmar Pfannenschmidt, the German sociologist and so-called laureate of alienation. My eyes lit up when I saw his name, as you will come to understand. But more of that later.

It's difficult for me to square Malcolm's circumstances then with his apparent eminence, whose true extent is only now revealed to me. I guess it's not how many copies you sell but who buys them. Somehow they kept up a house in the country: pokey and choked with books is how I imagined it. There were no children, although I didn't know this at the time. The obituary ends simply: 'He is survived by his wife Marigold'. Not for long, would be my guess. Deprived of an outlet, that mixture of fidelity and frustration will self-destruct in pretty short order. In my line of work you see it all the time.

It was Khaled, the postgraduate, who put me onto Malcolm's status as a scholar. 'A great man,' was his assessment, delivered after its subject had just left us on the stairs or outside the house – the setting is quite lost to me, only the words remain, together with the deep, accented voice that spoke them, each noun with its own little prow or stern of unnecessary emphasis. I don't think this opinion was based on anything as informed as a reading of Malcolm's books. Khaled's field was physics, I believe, but he was ridiculously star-struck by anyone who had appeared in print and this earned Malcolm a qualified exemption from his contempt, often expressed, for all aspects of English life. Khaled was a man tormented by exile, his mood tuned to the lurching rhythm of Arab fortunes, but too settled in our sleepy city to relish going home. The more comfortable he felt there the more he denounced us.

The high point in my relationship with Malcolm, the day I spent as his companion, provides my clearest image of him, and the only words I can definitely hear him say. I'm afraid I don't remember how it came about, but I am sure it was Marigold who put him up to it and so it may have gone something like this. We often met between our front doors, him returning from a stint in the library, me from a shift at some factory or building site, or perhaps from a day of carnage at the abattoir, the stink of death attached to my person like a curse.

'Good afternoon, young man,' he might have said, with ambiguous courtesy. 'Another day of wage slavery, I see. God rot their souls.' He remained a Socialist but had probably earned the right to be ironic about the class struggle, at least in the case of someone like me.

I can't imagine my reply. I'd grown used to bumping into him like this but our relationship seemed to have reached its natural limits and I don't suppose I did more than say hello. Which is why his next question wrong-footed me.

'Are you doing anything tomorrow?'

You need to understand that at any kind of distance his height was less of a factor, and he tended to be more playful and familiar when talking across the hall, the squares of its quarry-tiled floor like a court on which the moves were all verbal and in his favour. Even now I probably wasn't sure if what he had said was a polite expression of interest or the first part of an invitation. So let's say the rest of the conversation went like this:

'Er, no, I don't think so. Sleeping, mainly. Until the pubs open.'

'Come round for lunch, if you like. You look like you could do with a square meal.'

'That's very nice of you. What time?

'We'll need to do some shopping first. Say 10.30.'

That sounds about right, the offer expressed as a favour to me whereas it was Malcolm who needed helping. A shrewd old bird, that one, used to living on his wits. I'm not sure he'd ever held what you'd call a steady job, a way of life I was merely playing at and all too quickly abandoned.

On being admitted to their flat in the morning I discovered the real reason for my sudden popularity. Marigold was unwell and unable to leave the house. It must have been something quite serious because it was her job to keep them fed, clean, solvent and organised through good times and bad, in sickness and health, come hell or high water - the kind of woman, in short, who adds weight to all that folklore about feminine toughness and endurance.

Embedded in a plump armchair and bundled in a dressing gown from which her bare legs extended, unsettlingly smooth and pale, she made it known that Malcolm was unfit to buy food on his own, and that I had been called upon to hold his hand. There was a list and a purse containing the sum of money we would need. I was amused by her protectiveness more than the idea of Malcolm's ineptitude, which was surely exaggerated. But the moment we set out together I began to see him through her eyes. It was as if we were entering an alien world, the city centre a source of novelty and wonder. Household names were read out tentatively, like foreign words that might prove to be booby-trapped. The unloading of electrical goods from a lorry detained him for several minutes, his fascination like that of a child with no concept of embarrassment. Advertisements I hardly noticed any more were studied with a degree of care for which they were never intended, his intellect unable to take their slogans at face value, his subconscious new to the feints and sleights of mass persuasion. I was quizzed about the volume and legality of music blaring from shop doorways. He discovered traffic congestion, long after it had been invented.

The first stop we made was in what would now be called a convenience store but which Malcolm hailed as a corner shop of the type he remembered as a child. They were still quite common in the 1970s although even then their days were clearly numbered. I forgot what we bought, of course, and don't suppose you need me to imagine. But I do remember a long conversation with the woman behind the counter, her being wrong-footed by his rather obvious questions, the playfulness in his voice which may have been an attempt at flirtation. He was very animated as we came outside, delighted that shopping still retained its potential for social intercourse. I like to think of him using that word, which you can't say with a straight face any more, that is if it hasn't disappeared completely.

However, it was in the supermarket that his moment of revelation occurred. I have no idea which one it was, although I am sure the choice was more limited in those days and it would have been wretchedly small by modern standards. If you are too young to remember you will just have to take my word for it. Malcolm crossed its threshold with the nervousness of someone arriving at hospital for an operation. The rows of shelves without staff to attend them, the technical challenge of steering a trolley, the impression of abundance unmediated by human contact – it all astonished him. I clearly recall the thought forming in my mind: 'He has never done this before'.

And here was a man who wrote about the lives of ordinary people.

We queued up at the till where the arid, functional exchanges between customers and cashier visibly depressed him. As if to test a hypothesis he asked the girl about an item we'd not been able to find. The poor thing did her best to help but he was already shaking his head in disappointment. As we stepped outside into the bright July sunshine – or dismal summer rain: there's probably a website, if you're interested – he glanced behind him at the plate glass façade cluttered with posters advertising special offers and uttered the words that for years afterwards I associated with his name.

'I think Pfannenschmidt is on to something.'

It stayed with me, that remark. At the time it seemed amusing, proof of an endearing otherworldliness. Once I had got into business it stood for everything I mocked in people who learned about life from books. I never did get a degree and although I am now an employer of graduates, which ought to raise me above such feelings, something still rankles. The absence of letters after my name. Later I must have repeated it to my family, because it became a catch phrase to be trotted out when someone broke the mealtime taboo against being serious. And then, as the children grew up, it turned into a compliment, a verbal high-five for saying something penetrating or perceptive. Oddly, nobody ever asked who Pfannenschmidt was.

But I said nothing at the time. The remark was addressed to himself, and in any case I didn't have the confidence to take someone like Malcolm on at his own game. Nor have I to this day, despite what I've achieved. As you may have gathered I went the other way, into business. I own a couple of nursing homes, something I got into in the 1990s, by which time I had already acquired a bit of residential property. Tenant turned landlord, drop-out turned cop-out: one of those role reversals people joke about, usually as a way of making you feel guilty. Which I don't, by the way.

Of course I'm not so far off old age myself, now. Those headline birthdays with their surprise parties and holidays of a lifetime aren't the real eye-openers, I've discovered, the telling moments of transition. They happen when you are alone and there comes to you a vision of your own life as something whose pattern is decided, like a graph with enough co-ordinates in place to predict the future of the curve, so that its final shape, and the judgements others will pass, cannot be avoided. I'm sorry if that makes it sound like a profit and loss diagram: I've spent too long in the company of accountants.

And with this knowledge of the dice having been cast comes, for the first time, a sense of the world changing outside your control. Let me give you an example. My nursing homes run on part-time staff mostly. I can't afford it any other way. At the beginning there were students grateful for the money and nice middle-aged women returning to work. But now I have to recruit from anywhere: Poles, Russians or even farther afield. Good workers, on the whole, and who else is going to change old ladies' nappies for that kind of money? Not the English, that's for sure. Supply and demand: these are iron rules that hold us in their grip. I believe that as firmly now as I believed the opposite all those years ago. We're at the mercy of global forces. All the old ties of family and nation have been replaced by a simpler relationship, the payment for services rendered. But I see old men and women, people like my parents towards the end, bedridden and bewildered, struggling to understand the funny accents, eking out their last days in what must seem like a foreign country. You get a few that complain, women mainly, sour old biddies full of bile, but most try pathetically hard to catch what's being said, to do what's required of them.

I'm not complaining – it's how I earn a crust, after all. But you wouldn't be human if you didn't ask: is this really for the best? Where will it end? And lacking answers I wonder if I'm too close to things and it's someone like Malcolm I need, with a little more distance from the action. But here's the puzzle, here's what I don't understand. How do you step back from it all without losing touch? How do you begin life in the thick of things, hands dirty and bloody, literally fighting for a cause, and end up outside a supermarket with your jaw dropping at the sight of what has become of the world?

From our brush with modernity Malcolm and I headed back to Milton Street, me lugging the bags, him with barely-restrained impatience to tell Marigold what he had seen. But she was much less interested in the alienating effects of self-service shopping than in the contents of our carriers, which we offered up with a mixture of pride and apprehension, like Christmas presents to an only child. It fell to me to show her everything we had bought. The old girl sat forward in her chair and submitted the tomatoes to a suggestive fondling in front of my groin. She passed cheeses rather pointlessly beneath her blocked nose, with its little serif of dew forming at the end; and sniffed at the detergent we had come back with, the wrong brand of course, a mistake she fastened on as proof she was needed. Then she directed us in the preparation of lunch, during which Malcolm's odd little confessions of inexperience made the opening of a pilchard tin or questions regarding the edibility of cheese rind occasions for me to take over, embarrassed on his behalf and harassed by Marigold's sighs, bosomy and catarrhal.

Malcolm's bait to me the day before, the prospect of a square meal, was probably not too far wide of the mark as I generally ate meat pies in a pub or cold beans out of the tin. No doubt we had what passed for a salad in those days: cucumber slices, quarters of tomato, and lettuce all limp and clothy. You still get this apology for food served up by visitors to our homes, with their bedside picnics. Personally, I think we should have surrendered to the Italians in 1940: we would have got olive oil and garlic that much sooner. I don't remember the contents of a lunch over 30 years ago, of course, but what I have described has the ring of what I think is called poetic truth, down to the tinned apricots for afters, bland and syrupy, and what passed then for coffee.

I imagined my duty was done at this stage, with a little drinking time left before the pubs closed their doors for the afternoon. But I was invited to stay on to watch the tennis. Having no television of my own, and no interest in sport, I didn't know that it was men's finals day at Wimbledon, played in those far-off times on a Saturday. Malcolm and Marigold clearly saw this as an added bonus for me, and a further act of generosity on their part as they weren't fans either. I was too polite to disappoint them and I was also beginning to feel comfortable in their company.

You should realise that I had little contact with my own parents at this time. They were very old-fashioned and disapproved of my appearance, my lifestyle – pretty much everything. Later, when I became respectable in their eyes and they grew older and dependent on me, the gap between us narrowed. It was nice for my own children to have grandparents, but I never quite trusted them to say or do the right things and suspected Dad, in particular, of being a bad influence, always harking back to the good old days between the wars, a version of events which seemed complacent and self-serving even before I read about Malcolm's struggles. Towards the end I moved them into my first nursing home, and made a point of not treating them better than the other occupants. I passed this off as impartiality, especially as they weren't paying, but it had a small element of revenge in it, too, which I now find painful to admit. In any case, Malcolm and Marigold would have been about the same age as them, which could explain the unexpected feeling of reassurance and familiarity that came over me in their flat that afternoon, as if it was some sort of reconciliation.

The tennis is the reason why I can fix the date of this occasion so precisely. Danny, my eldest, who has a degree in physical education (which he has never used, by the way) explained to me once how sport provides shared memories at a time when all the other forms of common identity are breaking down. (I probably invoked Pfannenschmidt at this point.) The match was between Jimmy Connors and Ken Rosewall, that much I remember unaided. Two minutes on the internet enables me to identify the date, 6 July 1974, and the score. It wasn't a classic as a contest, one of the most one-sided finals ever in fact: 6-1, 6-1, 6-4. I've talked it over with Danny and it was, I am led to believe, a defining moment, when the old guard gave way to a brash new generation. Connors 21, Rosewall – I forget, but old enough to be his father. An oedipal contest, as Malcolm may have pointed out. The older man was the favourite of that geriatric commentator – what was his name? Full of deft touches but pat-a-cake stuff when compared to the energy and power of his opponent. And a face that gave too much away, contorted all the time by despair and self-pity. Whereas Connors was brutal:

no mercy and scant regard for tradition. Of course I was on his side, at least to start with. He was young and didn't play by the rules. But there was nothing love-and-peace about him either, so I was torn. Malcolm was divided in other ways. Instinctively drawn to the older player with his finesse and good manners, and with the added attraction, it became clear after only a few minutes, of being the underdog, he was also delighted by the insolence Connors offered to the establishment, with its royal box and Kipling clichés.

And so our allegiances wavered, not least in response to each other's changes of heart. The outcome of the match was never in doubt, and I think Malcolm eventually chose the historical position of any socialist in Britain, that of being on the losing side. I inclined towards Connors, but felt obliged to sympathise with the loser. Was this simply out of politeness towards my host? I must ask Danny what he knows about the psychology of spectators.

In case you think I have forgotten her, Marigold slept through much of the final, awaking now and then to comment on the physical attractions of the younger man. I somehow can't imagine her and Malcolm going at it, the affection between them having that wry, dry texture you get after years of marriage, so I don't think her innuendos were aimed at him, a reproach for failing powers. They remind me now of the old women I hear in my homes, calling out to the male staff, their lewdness more shocking, somehow, when it lacks the motive, the reference point, of sexual need.

That was the last invitation I ever had from the Benefers and I never set foot in their place again. Malcolm and I continued to greet each other across the hallway, with no increase in affection that I could detect, but Marigold I seldom saw and my services as chaperone were never needed.

There were a few changes to our little community before I left Milton Street, to move in with a girl I was keen on, although that didn't last. The young man I used to meet on the stairs disappeared, to be replaced by a couple who, as students, made being married seem like a daring breach of convention. And the middle-aged nurse moved on without ever clarifying the nature of her interest in me, beyond leaving a note apologising for not saying goodbye and wishing me well with all of my endeavours – another one of those words, like intercourse, that has, with their stiffness and ambiguity, gone out of fashion.

Khaled and his girlfriend remained. He wore steel-capped shoes that boomed on the bare wooden stairs and clopped across the quarry tiles in the hall. His approach was advertised by these ominous footsteps and by his habit of hawking loudly wherever he went, a punishment to the rest of us for the weather which made him suffer permanently from a cold, although the spitting itself was reserved for his own bathroom or for the gutter outside, depending on which direction he was headed. On bad days he barely noticed me or glowered as if I was to blame for something. But when his mood was buoyant he saluted me like an old comrade, and laughed knowingly as if I had just told him a joke or we shared some secret understanding.

Once away from the place I saw Malcolm less and less, and then not at all. You play the actuary with people you've lost sight of, the odds against seeing them again lengthening with the years until it gets to the point where you're sure they can't still be around. But now I discover that he kept going all this time, almost reaching his century. I can't help wondering if the milestone mattered to him, and how he was towards the end. But let's not go down that road. It leads to regretting that you didn't stay in touch, and before you know it you're thinking of how different your own life might have been.

And now here he is, the well-known, little-read writer on the one page where no one wants to appear. It's a modest write-up with an irregular, fitted-in kind of shape and the photograph of him looking the other way. He is in fairly undistinguished company, all of them held over from busier editions I suppose. A captain in some county regiment who held a bridge on D-Day and then spent the rest of his life running the family firm as if nothing had happened. The soprano notorious for a trail of unravelled marriages. And Malcolm Benefer (1912 – 2008). The obituary refers to illness in his final years, after a lifetime of almost unblemished good health. He might have ended up in one of my homes: now there's a thought. I could have talked to him. Held his hand. Made sure he had the best of everything. It's wishful thinking, I know, but I can't help wondering what would have passed between us, his voice weak and scratchy, my head bending closer to listen. His impressions of me as a young man, perhaps, which I find myself caring about strangely. A certain richness of thought which seems to have gone out of fashion. Or the sad parody of reason that most of my guests are reduced to, even the brainy ones.

But let's be honest, Malcolm couldn't have afforded our prices. And even if he had been under one of my numerous roofs I wouldn't have known. I may be in charge but they don't tell me everything.

Cupboard Love

Tina Freeth

There was a time when I used to love hiding in cupboards. I think I must have been around eight years old when I started seeking out the comforts of tall wardrobes and rolling myself up in the solidness of ottomans. They contained me, all of me. I was comforted when enclosed by something larger than I was. Even now, the fragrance of pine calms my nerves and dark spaces offer me solace. I remember listening to the sound of my own breathing; it was proof that I was alive. It was cupboard love, a wooden womb I could crawl into away from hurt and pain. Away from her.

Missy used to beat me with the feather duster. She held the feathered end, her grip so tight her knuckles shone red. She thought herself an artist even back then, her weapon of choice painting dark pink streaks across my back. 'Don't you ever talk back to me!' she yelled, 'you think she loves you but she doesn't! She loves me the most, you're not even her real daughter!' Perfectly formed parallel lines of pain. I used to run my finger along each one, trying to fathom how raised scars five inches long could explain her hatred.

Today, encased in a box of her own, Missy was buried. The sky opened up and wept all the tears that I could not. Still, I forgave her.

Nashville Shoeshine

Robert Ronsson

Sometimes I can be so self-absorbed even I think it's embarrassing. Take that sunny September Tuesday I had a lunch appointment in Nashville.

The limo glided into my drive at 6.15 am, bang on time. I was waiting at the screen door with my briefcase and overnighter. My overnighter – possibly the most compact wheeled suitcase in the history of travel; I was inordinately proud of it. An air stewardess had once asked me where I'd bought it. It was that cool.

We arrived at La Guardia departures as the first glimmers of day were lighting the underside of the Whitestone Bridge. I checked the screens. American Airlines 0693 departure for Nashville, 7.59 am – on time. I sighed and shook out my shoulders. It could easily have been a disaster. How many of my flights out of La Guardia had left hours late or been cancelled even?

Check in went smoothly and security was a breeze. I led my faithful Labrador of a bag down the slope to gate D4. The papers I needed for the day's meetings were in my briefcase and I read them through while checking out my fellow passengers. A full plane with masses of carry-ons would mean I had to position myself near the gate to be first on. I relaxed; not many New Yorkers were bound for Nashville that morning.

We boarded on time but there was a long taxiing line so we went wheels up nearly thirty minutes late at 8.27 am. We banked sharply and steered north-east with the flag-blue waters of the Long Island Sound beneath us. Once we had sufficient height we turned west in front of the Whitestone and, tracking the line of commuter traffic stalled on the Cross Bronx Expressway, we passed over the northern fringes of Manhattan Island.

The view levelled out and the plane settled into its route south-west along the Hudson towards Staten Island and the sea.

Manhattan lay beneath me basking in end-of-summer sunshine. It looked like a computer mother-board. The bare, green surface of Central Park lay at its core with soldered electronic pathways glinting. The lofty component of the Empire State stood twice as tall as the lesser circuit work. The silver hood of the Chrysler gleamed in the light from the east.

Heading south the cluster of smaller, less glamorous components in the processing zones of Greenwich, SoHo, Tribeca and Wall Street were silicon stubble beneath the soaring chip-towers at the island's southern point. These silver, flat-faced crags glinted with power as if I could see the currents surging through them. They pulsed with energy – the twin towers of the World Trade Centre.

As we swung round Battery Park and out over the Statue of Liberty I was exhilarated with a sense of being part of it. Born in one of London's poorest areas, here I was flying over the most vibrant city in the world. I lived in the epicentre of where it happens. The words 'New York' were in my address. How about that!

Beneath me, the Wall Street day was already under way. Men and women down there were at their desks trading billions of dollars in commodities, derivatives, risk vehicles, equities, currencies – you name it, anything on which they could make a turn. I, like them, was a Master of the Universe as I sank back into my seat and fell asleep.

The announcements telling us we were momentarily to arrive in Nashville was terser than usual. There was none of the gush about how wonderful it was we chose to fly American. I had my tasks on leaving the plane mapped out – shoe shine and rental car.

As we crossed the concrete flats of the airport apron and drew up to the gate there was no effusive 'welcome to Nashville' speech. We were simply told the flight and cabin crews would disembark first and a ground crew would supervise our exit from the plane. No problem. My only issue – did I have time for the shoe-shine?

The delay before taking off and a protracted journey meant I was in danger of being late for my lunch appointment. But my shoes were in desperate need of a shine. I had barely enough time even if there wasn't a queue at the booth. I knew where it was. If I got off the plane quickly and made straight for it I'd be on schedule, just.

I hurried up the ramp into the terminal. Other passengers in transit scurried round with mobile phones pinned to their ears. I put my head down and set a course for my shoe-shine.

To my relief all four chairs stood empty. The three black guys who ran them were huddled in a corner chatting. They didn't notice me. I climbed into a chair, planted my feet and coughed. One of the guys turned. He looked back to his colleagues and raised an eyebrow. I looked down at my shoes pointedly. He came over.

'You want a shine?' he asked.

'Yes.' I said. I gave him a look. Duh?

'Now?' he asked.

'Of course.' I said.

He shook his shaved head and put his fingers into the pot of black gunk. If he wasn't happy doing the job why not do something else?

He was polishing the shine on my first shoe before my irritation faded enough for me to notice the people talking into their mobiles as they passed. They zapped me strange looks as if to say, how could you?

I looked at the shoe-shiner's colleagues. They clustered round a portable television. The sound was too low for me to hear.

A sense of unease crept up my neck. 'What's going on?' I asked.

'Didn't you hear? A plane's flown into the World Trade Center,' he said, shaking his head. 'You didn't know?'

'What, a light plane?' I said. I pictured a businessman, late for an appointment, flying his private jet into one of the towers because he was on his mobile. Everybody was on their mobiles that morning. Perhaps it was time for me to cave in and get one.

'No,' he said. He looked up at me eye to eye as his hands moved furiously. I felt the contempt. 'It's a jumbo. Somebody flew a jumbo into the Tower. They reckon there's another twenty planes out there still unaccounted for. They're bombing America with our own planes.'

'Who?'

'Terrorists – maybe ours, maybe somebody else's – who knows?'

He worked in silence. I had to get out of that chair, find a phone and make some calls. The day was going to map out differently. Would the appointments happen? Would my evening flight to New Orleans leave on time? Should I go to the car rental place early to make sure they didn't let my reservation go?

But I couldn't move. I had to wait for the man to finish. You can't leave in the middle of a shoe-shine, can you?

An hour later, after I had made the calls and secured a rental car, I watched the television in one of the airport bars and saw the towers collapse. The horror unfolded. The carnage was happening while I was worrying about being late for lunch. Men and women were deciding it would be better to jump from 100 floors up rather than be burnt alive while I was wrestling with the problem of cutting short a shoeshine. My wife at home was certain it was my American Airlines flight and was trying to think how she would word the phone call to my mother in England while I fretted about the length of the queue in the car rental office.

And only later, when I knew the first impact had been timed at

8.46 am, did it occur to me that, for a brief moment, my flight, American Airlines 0693, and the fatal flight, American Airlines 11, could have merged as a single blip on a flight controller's screen somewhere south of the towers. The wings of the first terrorist bomb had been borne on the air I left behind.

First Loss

Gemma McErlean

For Paige's ninth birthday they went to the Wacky Warehouse and John threw up in the ball pit. He bought Paige a book about kittens because he knew she had two, called Missy and Tink. Paige said it was her favourite present.

On sports day Paige's mum brought her to watch, and she cheered when he came second in the wheelbarrow race with Steph.

Paige had a big brother called Robbie. He was sixteen and he'd carry her around on his back for ages, pretending she was a princess. Robbie was really good at drawing cartoon pictures, and he drew one of Paige on holiday in Tenerife. It had pink dolphins and purple kittens. Paige had it in a frame above her bed.

Paige was the second prettiest girl in his class and she was really clever.

Paige had leukaemia which is like cancer, and it made her really sick. Before she had leukaemia Paige had curly brown hair that went all the way down her back. When she was sick she wore a wig, and it was short and straight. It was still brown though.

Paige had been his friend since they were four years old. When Paige was nine and three quarters, she died.

John knew that she was really sick. He could tell because it lasted a long time and Paige couldn't do all the things they used to. She was too tired. His Mum told him that Paige got so sick that God took her up to heaven to take care of her himself. She said Paige wouldn't feel sick anymore, and she'd have her long curly hair back.

John was baptised a Catholic, and he went to Catholic school.

He'd made his Holy Communion with his class. With Paige. He didn't believe what his Mum said though. He thought, if God was going to make Paige better, why couldn't he do it here? Then she could go to school again and play with her friends at break time. And she could still have tap dance lessons, and go ice-skating on the weekend. She could have her tenth birthday at McDonalds like she wanted.

John felt all shivery when he thought about Paige.

When he went to Paige's funeral with his Mum, everyone cried a lot, and John cried a lot too.

When he watched Paige's coffin go down into the ground, he knew what his Mum had said couldn't be true. How can she be with God if she's buried?

John worried about Paige a lot. He thought she must be very scared. What if she was still sick, and she didn't have her Mum and Dad there?

John had dreams about Paige crying. It was really dark and she was on her own. John tried to talk to her but she couldn't hear him. Sometimes he woke up all sweaty.

There's a picture of Paige outside the Headmaster's office. It's in a fancy silver frame and underneath there's a poem that Paige wrote before she got too sick to come to school. It's about Missy and Tink. John doesn't like to look at it when he walks past in the morning. He doesn't like to look at Paige's desk either.

Miss Templeton got their class to write down what they remembered about Paige, and how they felt about her. It could be just a word or it could be a whole page, whatever they wanted. She told them they didn't have to write their names on them, and they could fold them up and put them in a box. Then she would take them out one at a time and read them, and if anyone wanted to share anything with the class they could put their hand up. John wrote:

It feels strange that Paige isn't here anymore because her laugh was the loudest out of all of the girls and it always made everyone else laugh. I think Paige wants to see her Mum and Dad, and Robbie. And Missy and Tink.

When Miss Templeton read it out, Luke Johnson put up his hand and said that his Mum had told him that Paige was okay because she was with God now. John wanted to ask Miss Templeton why God couldn't make her okay here, but he didn't.

Steph put her hand up and told the class that she had been round to Paige's house with her Mum. Paige's Mum had asked her if she could play with Missy and Tink because they were missing Paige a lot. She said they licked her hands like they used to do to Paige.

Their school is having a fundraiser tonight, in memory of Paige. John's class made 'P' badges to sell and there's going to be a raffle, and the money is going to a charity that helps children with leukaemia.

When he's getting ready to go, John's big sister phones to speak to him. He picks up in his parents' bedroom and closes the door. John's oldest sister is twenty one and of his two sisters, she's his favourite. She dresses cool and she likes good music, and she listens to him talk for hours. She said she preferred speaking to kids because most grown ups were actors.

That's why he told her about Paige. Told her everything.

At the fundraiser there were pictures of Paige, and everyone bought a 'P' badge. Most people paid double the price and they made lots of money for charity. Paige's parents, and Robbie were there, and some of the class sang Paige's favourite songs.

John was sitting with Steph and she asked if he remembered when someone pulled Paige's chair from under her in year three? Everyone thought she'd cry or get mad but she burst out laughing and couldn't stop for ages. This made John smile. Paige had played the same trick on him two days later. John, Steph, and some of the others spent the rest of the evening swapping Paige stories.

That night John dreamed of Paige but she wasn't crying. She was wearing her Communion dress and she had her long curly hair back. It was sunny and warm. She smiled and told him she was okay. She wasn't sick anymore. And she wasn't scared.

At school the next day, John looked over at Paige's chair and he pictured how she was in the dream.

When he next spoke to his sister, he told her, 'I think Paige is okay now.

Packing My Students Away

Kathleen Dixon Donnelly

This week I packed my students away.

The Vanessas and Jessicas, the Josés and Tonys. Their dreams confined to 3x5 cards, filed alphabetically, with no acknowledgement of their unique characteristics, in my grey metal card file (A through N) and a shoebox (N through Z).

On my way to the first university class I ever taught, 20 years ago, my boss handed me index cards and said, Have each one fill out a card; don't give essay tests. That was my only training. I told each student to write on the card his name, address, phone (more recently, e-mail), major, and ambition in life. These last answers fell in to a pattern.

'To have a family.' Usually from females.

'To be a millionaire.' Usually from males.

'To get my degree.' 'To be happy.' From both males and females.

The longest answers were from women returning to college, inspired to re-assess their priorities.

'If I can't get an A in every class I'll quit...' A bit obsessive.

'I want to be a good mom, but it's important to finish college, but I hate to leave my kids...' Heartfelt.

The most intriguing: 'To play the lead in a Broadway revival of *Medea*.' Where is she now?

When I taught in Ireland, the ambition part confused them. Not raised in a culture where children are asked 'What do you want to be when you grow up?' they would look at you as if to say, I want to be...*grown up*. There were no jobs, no future. Why *ambition*? These students wrote, 'To finish the course.' Now that the Celtic Tiger has roared (and gone back to sleep), would their answers change?

My favourite, from someone who had had me for several classes: 'To never have to answer this question on a card again.'

So as we pack to move to England, where I will have new students with new ambitions, I am finally filing all the cards from all the classes. Each assignment, each test grade, each group project is noted in my shorthand. When students have inspected their cards (certainly their right), they see a mish-mash of indecipherable marks. I see the class missed to take care of a sick baby, the mid-term exam done as a make-up because of a business trip, the team that gave the most amazing presentation.

As I integrate classes from ten schools in four countries into two boxes, some names jump out. She got her dream job. He's been promoted. Her name was in the paper, spokesperson for a politician. He's divorced and back in his old job. They line up in the box.

When I taught on Semester-at-Sea™, I had to use the index cards they brought on board; instead of 3x5, they are a half-inch taller. Mostly white, upper-middle-class Americans, their cards tower above those of the first-generation-college students from the Florida state university and the Pennsylvania liberal arts school. The names on the taller cards are of families who send their offspring to eight ports in Europe for the summer. The working class students spend the summer...working.

Sitting on our bed, I file, wondering, why bother? There are better ways to spend this time before we move. Will I ever need to know what Lisa got in Marketing? Which team Howard was on?

I feel obliged. Each class has been rubber-banded together since their grades were recorded on their school's computer. Tossed into a cardboard box, they have moved from my university office when I lost my job, to my home office, and then to my rented office downtown. They huddled together, daring me to file them. Now they are snuggled up on the bedspread with me as I sort, trying to connect each name with a face, a classroom, a college, a city.

Last night I finished. My card file and shoebox went into our storage unit, stashed with the desk and the chairs and the photos. On top I tossed the handmade cotton hamburger from the group that did the Burger King project. I don't remember their names. I don't remember their grades. I remember that they worked so hard to give a creative presentation and that they created this larger-than-life burger—with tomatoes, onions, and a sesame seed bun. I've never had the heart to throw it away. It rests next to the handmade M from the M&M's project.

Thirty cards have yet to be filed, from the students I am currently teaching. They will come with me, tucked into my carry-on, when we move to Britain. Once their grades are recorded, I will set the cards aside for safekeeping.

When our boxes from the storage space arrive in our new home in the UK, I will dig out the cards from this last American group, and co-mingle them with their predecessors, alphabetically. The Vanessas and Jessicas, the Josés and Tonys. I wonder how they'll all get along.

Stay tuned.

Contributors

Rena Brannan's poems and short fiction have been published in *The Harvester Anthology*, *Brainchild Anthology 6 and 7*, and the *SSU University Anthology*. She also has been short-listed for the Nichols Fellowship, Harper's Bazaar/Orange Short Fiction Competition and BBC Gloucestershire 10 Minute Shorts Competition.

Gabby Bulmer is a full-time teacher as well as a writer. She recently finished her first novel and is now in the process of submitting to agents. She is also collaborating with a student from the illustration course at Birmingham City University on a picture book, which is being entered for The MacMillan Children's Book Award.

Bobbie Darbyshire's debut novel, *Truth Games*, about sex in the seventies will be published in 2009 by Cinnamon Press. Inspired by the National Academy of Writing's screenwriting module, Bobbie has written the pilot episode of a TV adaptation of *Truth Games* for which she hopes to find a producer. Her work has been shortlisted in several competitions, published in *Mslexia* and performed by *Liars' League*. Bobbie lives in London and is working on a new novel.

Ryan Davis writes words to be sung or read. His debut album was released in 2007. He is currently working on his first novel 27; a story of rock and roll suicide, *God Bless The Child*; a screenplay, and a series of short stories about communication.

Kathleen Dixon Donnelly is a senior lecturer in the Business School at Birmingham City University. She relocated from Florida among four hurricanes in 2004 with her Irish Husband Tony and, eventually, two cats, chronicling the experience in *A Yank in 'Brum*, available at www.lulu.com/gypsyteacher.

Dave Ewer is a graduate of the Centre for Contemporary Cultural Studies at Birmingham University and a postgraduate student of Creative Writing at BCU. He is the author of the iconoclastic novel *DOG Sharon* – a satirical feminized retelling of the messiah myth situated in contemporary Birmingham, and is currently researching *White Punks on Dope* – a Cold War thriller set locally in 1978, featuring the fight to eradicate smallpox.

Tina Freeth began writing creatively in 2006 after friends commented on her lively and humorous style. In the months following Tina's admission to the NAW course, two of her short stories were published. Her short story 'Lychees and Bingo Balls' appears in the *Original Skin* anthology (launched at the Birmingham Book Festival in October 2007). A memoirist and fiction writer, Tina has recently started to write short screenplays and develop her knowledge of illustrated concept books for children. She is also a W. Wing Yip Brothers bursary recipient, given to students of Chinese heritage who excel in their chosen field of study.

After twenty years working as a teacher, soaking up stories, **Lucy Fussell** is now writing, reading and going for long walks in the hills. She is also training to be a counsellor. This is her first published work. She lives in the Peak District with her husband and her two youngest children.

Jackie Gay is the author of two published novels and editor of three short story collections. She teaches Creative Writing at Birmingham City University and for the National Academy of Writing. She is also a member of the British Paralympic sailing squad and hopes one day to sail for her country whilst fending off phonecalls from literary prize judges.

Bruce Johns works as Director of External Partnerships at Newman University College, Birmingham. A lifelong scribbler of unseen work, the NAW course has finally enabled him to get serious about writing. He is currently working on a novel, a family history and a number of short stories.

Fiona Joseph lives in Birmingham and is a former textbook author and university lecturer who now runs her own online publishing company producing learning resources for ESOL students. She was recently longlisted in the Happenstance Press International Short Story competition. As well as writing fiction she is currently working on a memoir, *Little B*, which gives an account of the life and pioneering work of Beatrice Cadbury, a member of the Cadbury's family of chocolate manufacturers.

Nick Le Mesurier has been writing for the last twelve years or more as an academic specialising in the delivery of health and social care services. Frustrated at the limitations of academic writing, he started writing fiction again about four years ago, and has published two short stories in Birmingham Words, www.birminghamwords.co.uk. He is currently working on a novel based on the experiences of child migrants to Australia in the 1950s.

Derek Littlewood teaches literature at the School of English, Birmingham City University. He is interested in possible connections between photography and writing. Swimming against the digital tide he hopes to convert his garage into a darkroom.

Gemma McErlean is a Youth Worker and Learning Support Assistant from Birmingham. She began writing at a young age but only recently found the motivation and confidence to share with others. She is currently working on her first novel.

Anthony Mellors is a Lecturer in the School of English. He is a noted poet and critic, with work published in leading poetry magazines and a critical study of late C20th poetry available from Manchester University Press. He is the editor of fragmente, a leading journal for poetry and poetics.

Nicola Monaghan is a novelist and Fellow of the National Academy of Writing. Her first novel, *The Killing Jar,* won a Betty Trask Award, the Authors' Club First Novel Award and the Waverton Good Read. Her second book, *Starfishing,* was released in March this year and will be followed up in June by a novella, *The Okinawa Dragon*.

Liz Nichols is an ex community psychiatric nurse turned college lecturer who writes to stay sane. Liz was shortlisted for the first ever 'Richard and Judy' short story competition and had a place on their 'Ticket to Write' cruise with Beryl Bainbridge and John Fairfax. She is currently working on her first novel.

Rachel Pickering lives in West Yorkshire, has two children and works in local government. She has had work published in Mslexia and since starting with NAW last year has had a story published in The Guardian. She has a particular interest in writing about women complaining.

Robert Ronsson's first novel *Year of Burning Hay* was highly commended in the 2006 Yeovil Literary prize competition but remains unpublished. He self-published *Olympic Mind Games*, a children's novel, in September 2007, after it was long-listed in the AC Black 2007 Novel Writing Competition. He is currently working on *The Spaniard's Wife*, a fact-based novel telling how the 1920 birth of a baby in a Glasgow tenement changed the course of British political history. It was short-listed for the Impress Prize for New Writers 2007. Robert also has had a number of short story competition successes since he started writing full-time in 2005.

Sophie Ward began studying with the NAW in 2007. She has a degree in English Literature and Philosophy and has written articles that have been published in The Times and Sesame Magazine. Sophie is currently working on a screenplay set in London and a book, *An Unreliable A-Z of Acting*.

Heather Wassall was born in the Black Country and graduated from Wolverhampton University in 2005 after studying English part-time. She is a part-time student on the MA Literary Studies programme at BCU. This is her first published work although previously her short story *24/7* was read at a *Short Cuts* literature event at Birmingham MAC.

Eveline Williams lives and works in London, where she attended writing courses at the City Lit for a number of years. She was delighted to be accepted into the National Academy of Writing. She now intends to do the work and take her love of writing to another level.